Paperback ISBN-13: 978-1-7359199-0-4
Paperback ISBN-10: 1-7359199-0-4

E-book ISBN-13: 978-1-7359199-1-1
E-book ISBN-10: 1-7359199-1-1

PDF formatted Book ISBN-13: 978-1-7359199-2-8
PDF formatted Book ISBN-10: 7359199-2-8

Audio Book ISBN-13: Forthcoming
Audio Book ISBN-10: Forthcoming

Printed in the United States of America

Shell Shock

PTS

Invisible Wounds

Battle Fatigue

VETERANS' REVIEWS

...it's changed my life in a positive way. My prior experiences... have not had this affect.

...thank God for angels like "John" who sacrifices personal and family time to help others be released from the "ghosts" that followed us home from combat hell

...needs to be offered to every veteran, with mental and physical benefits for everyone. I am in a much better place now than when I retired after +37 years in the Army to include 30 months in Iraq/Afghanistan

...my experience so far with the singing bowls; [the bowls] allows and trains or retrains the mind to get to a clearer state. I feel as a veteran truly wanting to start treating PTS. I believe this is the first step.

...this book guides anyone seeking to relieve stress and find peace, in a simple and straightforward manner. The artwork gives readers a visual understanding of the anguish too many people feel. John makes it easy to practice on your own by creating an acronym-CENTER-to guide your process. I also very much enjoyed the life guiding quotes he provided. The book mentions John's singing bowls, truly they need to be experienced to appreciate their powerful calming power.

TABLE OF CONTENTS

About the Author

Praise for the Author

DEDICATION

This book is dedicated to those who suffer like I do. We are in the repeating pattern of injured veterans dating back past Roman times, but this is our time to break that cycle. With knowledge we can heal, regain a healthy life and ensure the next generation has the key to understanding how to recover. We few who chose to defend our flag suffer silently. This suffering was a mystery to all of us. This book is dedicated to all the veterans that are hurting and still want to find a path to being healthy again.

To my team:
S- Thanks for being my rock and support
S- Thanks for the help with commas
S&SS- Thanks for putting me on my path
J- Getting me into class
L- Nice diagram
T- Your drawing skills are amazing

To my Vet groups- You have helped me more than I have helped you. Thanks for allowing me into your lives.

ABOUT THE ARTIST

Tim Crisman has graciously donated the illustrations in this book. I would like to thank him for donating his touching art, which demonstrates and brings into painful illustration the challenges and pain that we veterans feel.

When Tim is not sketching and drawing, he enjoys hiking and people watching in his spare time. Many of his art pieces are directly influenced by studying people in their natural surroundings. Tim loves recreating scenes and personalities in portraits and paintings. He also served his country with honor, thank you for your time and dedication to this book.

You can contact Tim at https://crisman-art.com/

1 Introduction

<u>Background</u>: My name is John Ferguson. I joined the Marine Corps at 19 years old in 1990. After serving 20 years and three tours I retired in 2010. I served two tours in Iraq and one tour in Afghanistan. During my service, I served in Tanks, Security Forces, Infantry and Artillery. The most challenging time during my service was with 1st Battalion 7th Marines. With 1/7, I deployed to Iraq twice (2004/2005 & 2006). Later on, I served with 3rd Battalion 12th Marines in Okinawa. While serving there I was deployed to Afghanistan (2008). I was part of an Embedded Training Team (ETT). That deployment was completely different from Iraq. We lived with and taught the only Afghanistan Army tank Battalion. The team I was on was training the Afghan's how to use Soviet tanks, the same Soviet tanks I was trained to kill. My tours took a toll on me and I struggled with the return after each deployment. My anger became something I feared. I knew as soon as I hit 20 years of service I had to retire. I was a mess and just needed to get away. Once I retired, I realized I was alone more than ever. I did not have my brothers around me nor was there anyone who knew what I felt.

During the years after my retirement, the transitioning into civilian life was pure anguish. For me, the civilians just did not understand. They were engrossed in their phones, televisions or electronics in some form. They valued themselves over others. We did not come from that world. We put our brothers and sisters first. We would rather see our comrades safe first. It was a different world and I felt distant and detached. I was lost, angry, confused and had

1

no patience. A few might read this and think we are very much alike; we are! I also felt like since no one understands me that no one cares. This is the very essence of why I wrote this book to tell you; YOU ARE WRONG, I care. I know the pain and want to help. YOU ARE NOT ALONE. If the anger, rage and disgust sound familiar, then we have answered the same call and chewed the same dirt. I have learned that no matter where OR when you served trauma is felt by ALL.

How to Use: This book is designed to be read in short bursts. With PTS, our attention span is almost nothing. Each "Chapter" is minimal so in the future if you experience trouble, you can reread that short chapter and without the frustration of searching for it. Once we get frustrated things start to be thrown, I tried to make the book easy to use so it does not become a flying object. If we can focus our mind on the issue at hand, we can reduce the problem down to a manageable size.

While reading this book, you will see where I repeat myself with the same words. This repeating is intentional as these are points I ask you to incorporate into your life. I speak often about Mind Nidra, but I will get into it later in the book. I have learned you need to understand these tools up front BEFORE you start to practice Mind Nidra. There were many tips I learned after I started my meditation practice that I wish I had known before I started. To avoid this pitfall, I first explain these tools to you and then we use them in a session. I also talk in depth about PTS and how it affected me. This will lead to more insight and understanding of PTS. When I talk to other veterans they open up and tell me they felt alone, like no one else felt the same way they do. I open up and tell you my story, so you know you are not alone and the way you feel is common among us.

No one ever taught me how to fix me. The following is the way I started to fix myself. I decided it was time I needed to fix me; get to living or get to dying and dying was not an option. Suicide will simply send the pain to others. Think of it like this, you have a heavy weight on your chest and can't breathe. That weight comes from our past events. If you go down that path, you end your pain, but in that very same second you take that weight and place it on your family's chest. Now they have to live with that weight that you could no longer hold. Plus, the worst part is our loved ones would never understand WHY!!

Basically, this is the roadmap of how I got from combat to Living Beyond PTS. There are expensive doctors who can rattle around in my attic, but they do not understand me. My question always was, "How could I find a way to live again?" I would spend hours, days thinking about a way out. After thinking about this long and hard, it came to me. There was no blueprint to follow! I knew I had to find the path and make myself healthy. I might not have had the how, but I sure as hell had the desire. With that desire, I pushed forward. Where this would lead, I had no idea, but one thing I knew for sure; something had to change. That desire was the spark I needed. Since you made it this far in the book, you have that same spark or desire to find peace.

My Fight to Living Beyond PTS: I was 42 and according to the doctors, I needed powerful medicine to get through the day. Just hearing this was a huge shock and not easy to accept. I had been poked, prodded, subjected to medical test after test, blood draws, MRI's, scans, doctors' endless questions just to hear, "There is nothing we can do". After letting that sink in, I decided there must be a way to heal the mind without powerful "mind numbing" drugs. I did not know it at the time, but my path was set, I was seeking a way to heal the mind.

After many years of suffering, I was struggling and had not found a way to heal. My symptoms were anger, anxiety, depression, isolation, detachment and hypervigilance. My get up and go got up and went. In a crazy twist of fate, a friend asked me to try his yoga class. My first thought was, "Great, let me twist myself into a pretzel, as if that could help." Then I will be twisted up and ticked off, not a great combination. I finally decided yoga had to be better than what I am facing now, ticking like a time bomb with no end in sight. The idea of living like that was getting to be too much for me. I had to find something now. After I got over myself, and with all the dignity that I could muster, I took a yoga class; not just any yoga class, but a veteran led yoga class. It was during this yoga class I found my first few seconds of peace and quiet. This was the moment that changed everything.

During that first class, my mind stopped spinning for a

few seconds. I focused on one thing, in that silence I found peace. No more patrols, no more rocket attacks and no more BS. It was just one thought. Take a few seconds and think about that...

Can you imagine what it would feel like if you had just one thing in your head?

Even for just a short time, you are controlling your mind instead of it controlling you. Controlling your mind is what this book and audio recording are all about; quieting the mind, learning to heal the mind then learning to control the mind. Once you start on this path to heal your mind, you can change your whole life towards the positive.

After my moment of quiet, I realized I needed more Yoga Nidra. I took another yoga class from my veteran friend. Months later we sat down, and he told me I should think about becoming a yoga teacher. Again, I thought that was crazy. After some reflecting and realizing that through yoga and meditation, I had made progress, I decided I needed to help other vets. I decided to become what there were so few of, yoga instructors dedicated to Veterans.

Off I went to yoga teachers' training. At first, it was another world to me. Eventually, I realized the instructors might have not walked where I had, but they had something we veterans desperately needed. They understood how to calm the mind. This practice of calming the mind was never taught to us. I thought back and looked at warriors in the past and focused on the Samurai. They were some of the most fearsome warriors to walk this earth, but they practiced meditation. The question was in my head, why would they practice meditation? After research, I realized that a calm mind before, during and after combat was key to their health. Meditation was just as needed as weapons proficiency.

During my teacher training, I learned about many tools that have been essential in my own healing. From physical poses to proper breathing techniques these formed the pillars of which I teach to other veterans.

My Intro to Singing Bowls: In the middle of my training, I was trying to meditate and then the spark happened. I was sitting down when a person struck a singing bowl. The bowl was used to signal the end of the meditation session. It was the striking of the bowl that made my mind focus on that sound. It was as if a life raft was thrown to me so I could stay afloat. I stayed in my position and just felt calm. I had been introduced to another world. This Yoga Nidra session with the bowl was even more powerful than my first experience. I was positive the singing bowls had to become a part of my teachings.

Upon graduation, I went to my local VA clinic and started to teach other veterans how to experience the same peace I felt. I bought three Tibetan singing bowls and began with three veteran students. Over the course of a few months, the four of us came up with a pattern of how to use the bowls. Their input was the key to developing Mind Nidra and the audio recordings. I used the knowledge from yoga teacher training and joined it with the sound of the singing bowls. The combination has been received with open arms by the current veterans. Now it is time to offer it to others, those who also need the ability to calm the mind, but are not located nearby.

This book is for all veterans, not just for combat vets. It is designed to help all veterans no matter the injury or challenge we face. Very few careers in the civilian life face the challenges we faced and continue to live with daily. In the beginning, I thought combat vets could not relate to any non-combat vets. I have learned I was missing the mark. I was so focused on my pain that I would dismiss others' pain.

FACT: I am not a doctor; I don't have a piece of paper hanging on a wall telling the world I can practice medicine. What I am, is a patient; my first patient. I refused the drugs the VA wanted me to take. I knew there was a better path; I offer this book only to show you my path. If you find peace through these words, then this writing experience has been a huge success.

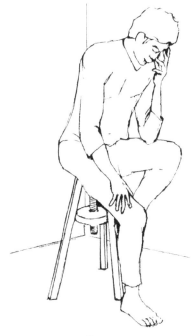

Purpose: The purpose of this book is to reach out to my brothers and sisters who face the same situation I live with; even to this very day. My hope is that through my words, you may find a path to healing. When that happens, I hope you find the strength to reach out to your brothers and sisters and help them. For now, let's focus on you; accept you deserve peace, which is a powerful first step.

"To hold it together when everyone else would understand if you fall apart... That's true strength." Miyamoto Musashi

Dark times are present and all encompassing. We don't want to hear "Everything will be alright." We cannot fathom that idea. I am here to tell you there is a way to get out of the darkness. There is an effective way to heal. No matter the injury, your mind can still heal. I ask only two things:

1- Come with an open mind (accept that not all cures come from a pill, a bottle or a needle)
2- I ask you listen to the complete recording. Finish the book first if you can (PTS limits our attention span). If reading is not something you can handle then put the book down, but listen to the 30-minute session. The audio recording has a greater effect if the book is read beforehand; but if you are drowning, then the 30-minute session is your life raft. Listen to the 3-minute "CENTERing" then start into the 30-minute session.

It may seem different in the beginning, but the results have been nothing short of amazing. I hope your journey to healing starts now. I hope you find your path to happiness.

Let's stop this spinning wheel together. Just don't quit on me, I want to hear about your journey.

<u>What is Yoga</u>: If you want the short answer here it is:

Yoga is about the MIND!

If someone told me 10 years ago, I would teach yoga (besides a lot of cuss words) I would have said "Ain't gonna happen Captain." I now spend my days teaching other veterans how to meditate and overcome their PTS.

Talking about yoga is one of the major hurdles I have when talking to veterans. Just the word yoga and people turn and run. I am not asking you to start a physical yoga practice. I am simply taking one part of yoga and extending that tool to you.

To sum up the yoga that is offered in the book, yoga is about the MIND. The physical poses are useful, the breathing is useful, but when all the aspects of yoga are combined their end goal is calming the mind. Yoga is a practice that focuses on helping, calming and healing the mind.

If you want a deeper understanding, then read the book and use the many other tools that are offered. Please don't get wrapped around the word yoga. I am not a skinny woman in tight pants asking you to do crazy things. I am offering some of the best tools that helped me get through my days and ultimately to Living Beyond PTS.

One of the things that drew me to continue studying yoga was that I actually experienced a few seconds inner peace while meditating. That to me was worth more than gold. Imagine a time where your mind does not feel like a hamster on a spinning wheel. Our mind spins here and there with no relief in sight. To slow the mind, we artificially stimulate it with drugs, alcohol, sex or shopping (see Chapter 2 under "Chemical Altering Game"). Now imagine a time where you can slow your thoughts down to a point where you are not in pain or worn out trying to figure it all out. One of the most important aspects of yoga I learned is "yoga is about the mind." I will explain why that is so important in a moment.

What is Yoga? Yoga is a practice that is 5,000 years old. It was designed to allow people to find a healthier lifestyle through stretching the body and focusing the mind. In today's culture, yoga has become a watered-down shell of its true roots. Yoga has eight limbs; each supporting each other till the person reaches total peace, (Sumadi "Pure bliss.") Most people think of just the physical poses as yoga, but there is so much more to the practice of yoga.

Today's yoga is more about the physical movement and less to do with the mental aspect. I have seen many times in current yoga classes, skinny women in tight pants doing impossible things. This outward appearance keeps many veterans away from yoga. The basic goal of yoga is to quiet the mind. How this is done? Start with stretching the body. As you sit there right now somewhere on your body is hurting. That pain has your attention. When the body is in pain, the mind cannot relax. The mind not relaxing keeps the hamster wheel spinning and we cannot find peace. In yoga, once you learn how to stretch the body, the body can remain in one place without pain. Once the body is without pain, the real work begins. Now we move to the mind stuff and slowing this spinning wheel. How do we stop the spinning wheel? We train the mind to focus! Through this book and into the practical application (the audio recording) the technique to quiet the mind will be discussed. Through yoga, you could reduce or come off your medications, stop with alcohol or drugs and find

10

happiness. If someone told me that information years ago, I would say go pound sand, it's not possible. Here I am living proof, if I can do it anyone can, especially you.

You are not alone.

2 FALLOUT

One thing I have learned from talking with other veterans is even though the details of our experiences were different; the pattern of our lives was the same. We went off to war, we left loved ones behind, we were trained to survive; but once we returned, we were not the same. Some received life altering physical injuries. Now we all live with the nonvisible wounds. These wounds cannot be measured, nor are they the same for each person.

PTS!   D?: Notice I said PTS (not PTSD). In my opinion, we do not have a disorder, what we have is an event or events in our lives that comes to the surface. Other people may have broken bones, dyslexia, the list is endless, but they are not named "Disorders." If we break a collar bone, the doctors do not say this is Broken Collarbone Disorder, it is simply called a broken collar bone. I do not like to hear I have a disorder; I went forward to defend my country and these events will be with me for the rest of my days. It is not a disorder; we chose this life, but I will not accept that I have a disorder. Doctors are happy to say this is a disorder and label me broken. That is not acceptable, I am not broken. I had my pieces rearranged, that is all. What I do have is an opportunity to overcome an event in order to become a better person. When we accomplish something, we feel better. It may take months or years, but this is my path now and I will walk it. I hope I do not walk this path alone.

Hypervigilance: The training we received taught us to survive by being ever ready. This is the very beginning of hypervigilance. Hypervigilance is what some call being "on guard." We stay in this state as a way to protect ourselves from danger. We relied on hypervigilance to get us through our hardest times. While we were serving, we stayed on guard constantly. In order to always be ready to fight, our bodies released natural chemicals to aid in this process. The chemicals such as cortisol and adrenaline alter both the body and the mind. The chemicals that flowed through us to aid in combat are still flowing through us now. If you are dealing with PTS, anxiety or anger, than understanding those chemicals will allow you to move forward with your healing.

When we return home, it is not the same. Families have grown and gotten along without us, skills we used in the military may no longer be useful, people from our home do not understand our frustrations and we don't understand

14

ourselves enough to explain our feelings. We no longer fit into our home which is threatening and scary. When we are threatened, we rely on hypervigilance to continue to get us through. I think of this feeling as being in the primal state.

Hypervigilance for me meant I could not be near crowds or hear loud noises. I could not have people stand behind me. I needed to sit in a corner so no one could sneak up behind me. I would start sweating for no reason. After I would go through one of those situations, I was exhausted. I used so much energy to get through the situation (nail my feet to the floor so I did not run away) that I had no energy to be a husband or a dad. I would just hide, wanting to sleep, but knowing that would lead to another fear. That fear of closing my eyes and facing the nightmares. It was like an evil circle, when I was near people, I had to burn energy to just "act normal". I had no energy to "be normal" with my family. I needed to recharge, but I couldn't for fear of nightmares. Thus, I slipped further into my black hole. I felt like I was scraping the bottom of the barrel. My family endured my deployments and now I could not even be a good husband or a good dad. I owed my family, but I could not repay their support. What kind of a shit was I?

The Primal State: In the primal state, the basic five senses are used to navigate through a problem. We depend on this primal state. We see, hear, taste, feel and smell things on this basic level to survive. Love is not a basic state, so it is cast to the side. Tenderness, understanding, romance and empathy, were things we did not rely on to survive. We focus on the primal instincts that got us through. Love, compassion and understanding were not needed in our past, BUT these emotions are needed NOW to get us back to living again.

15

Primal state - allowed us to survive.

Emotions - allow us to thrive, once we allow them back into our lives.

We lived in this world of constantly being on guard to protect ourselves, but we have now dragged our loved ones into this world.

Imagine your loved ones going on patrol with you.

This idea may seem farfetched, but they are being subjected to our actions, words and emotions. They could not understand, yet we are frustrated when they don't understand us. We, the ones who went forward, did so of our free will. They did not make that choice, but still support us even when they do not understand. They want to understand, but for them to understand, we need to tell them what we are feeling. We might not be able to explain our experiences, but we can explain our feelings. Just saying," I feel overwhelmed" "I feel detached," or "I feel angry" is a great starting point.

SUGGESTION: In time you will get to where you can explain why you feel the way you do, but for now let them in on the basics. Let them try to support you in a better way... the better way is hearing from you. In the beginning, my wife and I had a word that we used to communicate anger. It can be anything such as bird, red or whatever. We used it as a signal that either I was angry and needed space or she noticed my anger and I should step away before I blew up. This allowed us to communicate without an explanation.

Primal state- How we survived

Chemical Altering Game: The body runs on chemicals (endocrine system) to keep us alive. When we have a traumatic event, the brain has issues with the proper balance of chemicals. Doctors prescribe medications that a majority of veterans take to deal with issues. Some veterans choose another route. Some veterans try to stop the pain by using drugs/alcohol, turning to sex or shopping/eating or as some call it, "self-prescribing." Every one of those actions causes a chemical reaction in the body. Alcohol and drugs are depressants; the body slows down to the point that we think we can "handle life."

Sex, shopping, or eating causes a chemical reaction, but instead the body is excited, and endorphins are released. This happiness is a temporary condition and we will have to go back for a larger "dose" to reach the previous level of happiness. Then regret and or suffering creep back in, and ultimately, we go deeper into our hole. One-step forward two steps back. Sound familiar? If so, you are not alone.

STOP & THINK- "People are not addicted to drugs or alcohol; they are addicted to escaping reality." – Unknown author

This primal state of increased awareness is where we incurred our injuries; those injuries are still affecting us now. That injury has caused our body to be in a constant state of being in survival mode. So naturally, when life is at its worst, we revert to the very state that got us through our hardest time. In the primal state, we were hypervigilant and on alert. We keep that going, as we are running out of ways to cope with life.

Anger – No Way Out:

"Anger is a punishment we give ourselves for the unchangeable past or the unknown future." –Unknown Author

Those who suffer with PTS feel as though anger is always present, just sitting below the surface ready to rear up and burn the world we know. We feel trapped; as though no other person could possibly know what we face. What is the reason for anger? Put simply, anger is EASY.

Anger is a primal emotion. It protects us by getting us ready to fight or take flight. Anger always lurks below the emotional surface. Of all our emotions, it is easy to become angry. On the other hand, what we seek is at the other end of the emotional scale. It takes work to achieve happiness or peace and, in most cases, the "task" of being happy seems too hard to reach.

Anger is socially accepted. When people interact, emotions are displayed. Happy – smile, sadness – tears, depression – slouching, or anger – fists clinched and shoulders up. Our society expects us to not to show taboo emotions, such as sadness, depression, etc., but anger is widely accepted.

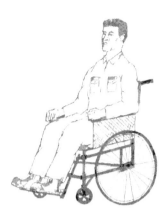

We can take our emotions of sadness, depression and then outwardly display them as anger for all to see. We accept anger. We use it as a shield to protect ourselves. However, we are only fooling ourselves and allowing that emotion to eat away at our self.

FACT: Here is something for you to think about. What is the opposite of anger? This was a question posed to me and it stopped me in my tracks.

At first, my mind came up with peace. Yet to achieve peace, I found I needed happiness. So if happiness is a building block for me to find peace, how do I get happiness??? In the beginning, this may be a small point or maybe you don't care, but over time I hope you will look back and give your input on this question.

What is the opposite of anger in your mind?

We who live with PTS are physically and mentally worn out just living day to day that we cannot even imagine being happy, much less, actually being happy. We feel at the end of our rope. That happiness, the very thing we desperately want, is too hard to obtain. Every day we wake with a secret desire to reach new heights of being at peace;

or we hold the flicker of hope that today we will break out and find happiness.

When I say anger is easy, you of all people understand what I mean. Anger is like air; it is everywhere. Anger is an easy emotion to utilize and one of the most destructive. Anger not only makes us worse, but it hurts the ones we love. In turn, hurting them makes us even angrier. Thus, the ugly cycle keeps spinning.

Get angry → Primal state →Words and action no longer matter → We hurt others → We regret our actions → Try to reaffirm our goal of peace → Run into frustration → **Get angry**

What would you say if I told you the cycle could stop? You just learned a very important lesson. Anger is easy. With that knowledge, you can reflect on your actions and move closer towards peace by admitting it to yourself that anger IS a problem, anger DOES live inside you, but it does

NOT DEFINE you.

FACT: This was a sticking point for me. To admit I was angry took a lot of energy and time. It was like climbing Mount Everest with a 100-pound pack on my back. Once I admitted to myself that I was angry, the pack came off my back. I accepted that I was angry.

A good friend of mine explained their anger in a way I felt I had to pass on to you. My friend's anger was a protective wall. That anger would provide protection, but at the same time would not allow my friend to move past the issue. Anger filled that person up. By filling them up, it also brought the fear of losing that anger and creating an "empty hole" where the anger used to live. What will take the place of the anger? There would be a big empty spot if this anger leaves the body. This is a key point.

Acknowledging that we fear to lose the anger for fear of what will take its place. Anger protects, but it does not heal. Holding the anger is holding you back from happiness. Only you can define you. Anger can also be thought of as a lack of knowledge or understanding.

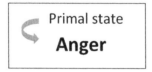

"Anger doesn't solve anything. It builds nothing, but it can destroy EVERYTHING." -Thomas S. Monson

3 ANGER & IDENTITY

<u>Negative vs. Positive</u>: For me, negative versus positive was simply good versus evil. To me, positive was good, Negative represented bad and what we do not want. So, when I was filled with negative emotions, I thought of myself as evil, mean and a bad person. I would think, when did I become evil, or mean? The events that resulted in our PTS place us on a path of anger and frustration.

Here we go again, another never-ending circle. I got mad about anything, I felt anger constantly. I became more negative; thus, I must be evil and mean. I was swimming in a pool of negative. Everything was negative. I could not even muster One Positive Thought. I finally got tired of seeing myself as evil. I wanted to change, that change came from seeking positivity. I lived negatively with nothing good coming from it, so I needed a new path. That path is positivity. I say this so you understand one of my biggest challenges, I felt as if I was evil. You are not evil! You are seeking a way to heal that has never been broken down by someone who is just like you. It seems as if doctors cannot put actual PTS events together with a path to healing. They offer treatments, but they don't understand that cause. I have seen both sides of trauma and the healing path.

FACT: Anger is a useful tool, but unchecked it has devastating results. Unchecked anger is degenerating and debilitating. Happiness takes work and can be elusive as catching smoke. Still others internalize that anger and that morphs into another challenge, depression.

During a meditation session with the veterans, one veteran was disturbed with visions he had during meditation. These dreams/visions are a big reason some veterans can't sleep. We listened as this veteran told us of the visions. Speaking of lost friends in Vietnam and carrying these visions to this day he said, "I couldn't get them out of my head, they are always there." We know that pain VERY well. Here are a few points I brought up to help him acknowledge the issues he was facing.

1- The event happened, and we were never prepared to handle it. We were told to "just deal with it" or "suck it up buttercup".
2- We are besieged by emotions (fear, sadness, rage); we don't understand what is going on, so we display our emotions as anger.
3- Living with these emotions disguised as anger for so long has become our perceived image; it is now how you see yourself.
4- These emotions masked as anger are how we feel we must live our life. Anger is now our identity. If we lose this anger, then we are losing our personal identity.

No person wants to lose his or her identity. Thus, we keep the anger so we can keep our identity. The circle keeps us trapped.

Event → Emotion comes out as anger → Held so long becomes our identity → Refuse to lose our identity → Live with event → Circle back to memories of the event going endlessly

BREAK THE CIRCLE: Replace your self-perceived identity. The following section is the breakdown of how to help you break the circle.

Acknowledge, Knowledge, Act: To replace our self-perceived identity; **acknowledge** the event. Acknowledgement is neither positive nor negative, but it is simply saying this event happened. Many emotions surface when we think about our events. Letting the emotions come up is hard, but over time you will be able to look at the event and just witness the event as an impartial judge.

With that impartial observation of **acknowledgement**, you now have **knowledge** of yourself. That knowledge allows you to move forward with two points. The first point is how you feel about this event, you don't have to say it out loud, but admit it to yourself. This event happened and this _____ is what I feel. This feeling you have admitted to yourself may change over time as you grow, but you are **acknowledging** your event and armed with that **knowledge** you can handle the emotions. That knowledge allows you to **act** by having compassion for YOU! This is where you can break the cycle; this is where you choose to move towards your new path, the path of happiness and peace.

You have the power to **act**. Your **act**ion may be small, only a simple "OK, I now see this process inside me" or maybe on a greater level "I am at peace with this event". Either way you are now healing, that is all that matters.

Event happened – **Acknowledge**
I feel this way – **Knowledge**
Compassion / Understanding – **Act**

Acknowledge – Knowledge – Act

27

KEY POINT: Slowly over time, the acknowledgement will turn into a desire to start to heal. This desire is the long road we all must travel. We are waiting for that desire to come to us. First we need knowledge to make us better. A lack of understanding keeps us in the same circle. If we don't know what is hurting us, how can we fix it? Thus, "desire" is the long path we are on. Now you have the knowledge and understand yourself a little better.

This key moment "desire," is signaling your internal self-wanting to move towards a positive path. We will never forget our event/events; Rockets, Mortars, IED, friends left behind, Military Sexual Trauma (MST), etc., but we can loosen the chokehold this event has on us. When we learn what is happening inside, we can work towards becoming healthy again. Supported with the knowledge you have of the emotional circle you can move towards a positive path.

Revolve or Evolve
Revolve= keep spinning in the same place
Evolve= growing, learning, healing

IT IS YOUR CHOICE; YOU HAVE THE POWER!

Further down the road you will face your problems and open your trapdoor where past events are stuffed (see Chapter 12 under "Good vs. Bad"). For now, a better understanding of our emotions that surface as anger that leads to a new identity, the resistance to losing one's identity. Breaking that circle with Acknowledgement, Knowledge and Act should allow some personal insight into how we deal with our event.

Our challenges- (What happened) Patrols, Rocket

attacks, the actions that took place that we live with.

Emotions- (How we behave from those challenges) our reactions/behavior to our challenges. Our emotions may be presented as anger, verbal abuse or physical abuse.

Further down the road we will look at our challenges themselves that are holding us down. For now, if we acknowledge our emotions that surface, we can take an important step towards healing. Breaking that circle with Acknowledge, Knowledge and Act.

The Fog: A veteran came to me after a session and asked to speak privately. We stepped out to a quiet place. With his head hung low, he told me he was mad at himself because he cannot do what he used to do. He went on to explain he "hides" in bed and can't get out of bed at times. He cannot concentrate or focus on things that he knows needs his attention. His wife was supportive but she could not understand how the man she married, the man who provided, now cannot even do simple things.

This conversation hit me like a ton of bricks. I too suffer from this issue. I call it "The Fog". It is a code word I use with my wife on my bad days, the days I cannot focus enough to tie my shoes or leave the house. I now look at "The Fog" as my mind telling me to meditate. When the world speeds up, I must slow it back down so I can take my place in it. This code word helped my wife understand a few things, one- I am struggling with basic things right this second. Two- I may or may not need help (I will let you know). Three- shield me from the world (she always has my back). By letting her know I am struggling, she can support in a way good for both of us. It is no longer me versus the world; it is us facing this challenge together.

SAFE WORD

The 'Fog' is real and comes in many forms. Some vets may experience it to a higher degree. The main point is you are not alone, at first I felt so alone and ashamed. Now that I see this same issue in other veterans, I realize I am not off my rocker. The 'Fog' is real; I was not making things up. To hear another vet talk exactly like I felt was huge for me. In that moment we shared our "weakness" and we became stronger by knowing we are not alone. Others experience this feeling too. I have many goals of this book, but for this chapter, I hope you take this 'Fog' portion and see others feel this way. Maybe you have others issues I haven't experienced or written about. I hope you share your experiences on my Facebook page so others will read your story and grow from your past. Together we will pull ourselves out of the darkness.

STOP & THINK: Anger suppressed becomes depression.

To hear another's perspective on how they healed, allows you to form your own opinion, thus free yourself from the yoke of self-imposed prison. Here is a saying I offer you to think about:

"One of the marvels of the world is the sight of a person sitting in prison with the key in their hand." - Rumi

At first, we do not even see the prison, and then over time, we do. We wonder how we got here. How do we get out? The how we get out can take years, but finally we focus the mind and see the problem for what it is, and then the problem can be overcome. The day comes when we stop beating our fist on the wall screaming to be let out. We reach our hand into our pocket and there it is; the key we have been searching for the whole time was within our grasp.

Physical Health vs. Mental Health: If I say the words mental health, what comes to mind? Insane asylum, need to see a shrink, wacko, lost your marbles? That is what most people think, but why?
If I say the words physical health what comes to mind? Running, weightlifting, there are many ways to make the body healthier and stronger. Why does that come to mind?

That is what we have been told since day one. Eat right, stay active and live longer, but no mention of mental health as a way of living longer. I look at the human body as an RV (Recreational Vehicle). Our RV takes us places, we fill it up (eat), we do maintenance on it (Physical health), we use our RV for pleasure, but the RV still needs a driver. I will offer this view; the body is just there to move the mind from place to place. The RV does what it is told do by the brain. So why is the brain (mental health) looked at as taboo? Because that is what we have been told from the beginning. We have not learned nor been taught that mental health is more important than physical health. As the body is the RV, the mind is the driver. When the driver is calm, the RV will operate properly. When the driver is angry, the RV will operate erratically. We need to look at

the mind and body and realize they both need to be provided ways to become healthier. Mental health is not taboo, it is key to living a longer healthier life.

Our minds will pull us this way and that way. In the beginning, when you try to control the mind through meditation or breathing practice, the mind will drive erratically. When the driver and RV are not in sync, we get frustrated, abandon the practice and do something else. Most likely,

33

the something else is TV, smart phone, loud music, drugs or alcohol. These are all ways to distract the mind (escaping reality), but those ways of distracting the mind are not controlling the mind. When you start Mind Nidra, look at this like a meal. You sit down for dinner and you get a 10-pound steak in front of you. Your first thought is no way can I eat all of this. We must start somewhere, so take small bites of the shorter meditation sessions. Keep going and your time will increase to the point where you look forward to meditation. When that happens, you know you are focusing the mind.

The Power of Self-Reflection: Where that anger comes from is the question we will address now. We know anger hurts, but moving to the next step of self-reflection will allow us to not repeat our past mistakes. Our anger is collected from shame, sadness, loneliness, desperation, jealously, loss, MST, etc. The next time you are angry and then cool off, try to understand where that anger came from. We display anger to keep people away, to keep people from asking tough questions or just from frustration, because people around you don't understand you and your past. Anger can be thought of as your shield. You use your shield to protect yourself, but what happens on the other side of the shield (to our loved ones) can be devastating.

The real issue here is WHERE did that anger come from? You can start to look inwards and see that anger is easy, but taking a deeper look and admitting what the real issue is: shame, guilt, fear, etc. will lead you to your place of peace. You do not need to admit this aloud, but admitting it to yourself is a huge step. The power of understanding what is happening in your brain through self-discovery is another stone from which you can rebuild your life and embrace Living Beyond PTS!

Some veterans who did not face combat also feel shame, the shame of not going forward into combat. We all raised our right hand and swore to defend the Constitution. Where we were placed was never up to us, we just went where the "Coach" put us. Where the coach put us depended on how we best supported the mission. Some go forward and some don't. If you raised your right hand and took the oath, then you did your country proud. Combat is a way some served, no veteran is better than another veteran just because of where the coach put us. Combat does not prevent someone from getting PTS. We all suffered, but few know how to heal.

Primal state
Anger
Fog

<u>What We Face With PTS</u>: I touched on this earlier and think we need to talk about this more. PTS has a stigma attached to it. People viewed me as damaged or on the edge as if I "could snap at any time." Just that made me even more ticked off. PTS is something we live with, but it does not define us for the rest of our days. We saw things, experienced things that most could not even fathom, but we are still here and trying to pick up the pieces of our lives. PTS is real, it is difficult to diagnose, and PTS is hard to treat. Doctors want to throw pills at us, or we use alcohol and self-medicate to escape reality.

FACT: Drugs and alcohol are just the tools to escape.

Alcohol and drugs are not weakness; the lack of knowledge about why we do what we do and use what we use is the major issue.

We get out of the military and know we must keep putting food on the table. We will pull our share and do what is right. We put off treatments as the job will not give us time off or they cost too much for us to afford. I work with many Vietnam vets and in my opinion, they were treated the worst. After fighting, they came home to people spitting on them. They closed off to the world and headed into work to distract them from the horrors they walked through. Now they are retired and cannot keep up the fight. I want to help them, but also help the heroes I walked with in Iraq and Afghanistan. I don't want to see the Operation Iraqi Freedom (OIF) and the Operation Enduring Freedom (OEF) veterans or any vets continue this circle. Many veterans work until they can't and then when they are aged and retired, then they seek help. This book is designed to be used on your time with minimal cost. Unlike medications there is no refill charge, just listen to the audio recording. Listen until your body is comfortable and your mind focuses.

PTS comes from living in the fog. The fog comes from anger (and many other emotions we don't display or acknowledge). Anger is created from the event in our life that has changed us. The primal state was one we lived in just to get to the next day. Knowing the flow of how we reached the PTS state will make living with it a little easier.

Snapshot in Time: The events that cause our PTS are etched in our minds. We save not just the action, but we save the time of day, all the people involved, what the temperature was, what the air smelled like, who was where. Everything slowed down and was stored in our brains. Then to protect ourselves we place those events in our closet marked "do not open". Some may even bar the door and put on a padlock to ensure it never opens. The hard parts is when this closet busts open from time to time and we see, feel, hear everything from those events. That is where our anger, frustration or lack of sleep comes from. It is that closet we fear due to the unknown. How to overcome the closet is in Chapter 12 under "Good vs. Bad". For now, just knowing this should help you move forward on your path.

A Cup of Anger: When we feel physical or mental pain, we want to get rid of it as quickly as possible. Our anger is the pain we feel inside from our past events. We feel it and want to get rid of it. We do and say hurtful things to try to ease our internal pain. For example, you hit your hand with a hammer, now you have pain. You want to get rid of the pain, so you throw the hammer at the ground. The hammer feels no pain, but that action is you "throwing" your anger somewhere else. We do this with loved ones or those who are closest to us.

You received pain from past or present experiences (combat, MST, work, bills, etc.). Now the pain is in you and you want to get rid of it. We send our one cup of anger to our loved ones. It does not have to be physical it can be emotional or mental (words or actions that hurt).

Your loved one receives the hurt or pain and wants to get rid of the anger, so they pass it right back. This time, they add more pain into it, now it is a cup and a half. Then you not only have your original hurt, anger or pain returned to you, but there is more of it. Thus, the cycle keeps spinning. Knowing what you are doing and why you are doing it will help you to find a way to stop this behavior.

Tips: Instead of yelling, try walking

away.

> Use your 3-Part breath
> Tell the other person you are mad to let them have some glimpse what is happening

<u>Don't Save the D-A-T-E</u>: When an event is going to happen, people ask you to save the DATE so you can be at their party or event. They want you to remember to join them. For us, the D-A-T-E represents **D**epression, **A**nger, **T**rauma, **E**xtreme anxiety. It is the DATE we are trying to avoid, ignore and hope it all goes away. We often associate our lives with the very definition of DATE. Everything is **D**epression, **A**nger, **T**rauma and **E**xtreme anxiety and we get stuck in this endless chain.

In the previous chapters we have spoken about how we got this way, why we react the way we do and how to start to recover. Just by simply knowing these facts should offer you a helping hand. Now by realizing we *don't* have to save the DATE; we move forward in little steps. By understanding all of these complex issues, we can step back and look at ourselves from an unbiased position. We can see why we act the way we do, understand that these actions/emotions are not something we were ever taught, thus something we have no idea about. With knowledge comes power, this power will enable you to start to heal. Knowing what is wrong and why it happens allows us to move forward to fixing it.

FACT- We have all been told "Calm down." Just that statement sends me up a wall. To me I think, "This **is** calm, if you want to see the opposite stand by here it comes." Now think about this.................how many times were you taught how to calm down? Told vs. Taught!

The answer is most likely never.

The act of being uncalm is a physical one. There is no thinking, just tapping into our anger and PRESTO we are doing what we do best, rage. The lesson of how to remain calm is a mental one. It is that half a second pause we have; that half a second when we go from mentally frustrated into physically acting out. This half second can keep us from doing something we will regret. So how do we remain calm?

First, think on this, we cannot calm the storm, stop trying.
What we can do is calm ourselves and the storm will pass.

Remaining calm is the gift you give yourself.

We needed to focus our mind to solve our problem. Mind Nidra is that focus you need. It allows you focus on one thing. At that point, rebuilding our lives seems doable.

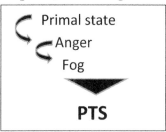

We were diagnosed with PTS, but we had no real understanding of the enormity and complexity of this issue. Now you should have a better grasp of what PTS is. Now we move to learning tools to address PTS.

4 Roadblocks

In this chapter, we will look at how to start to heal the mind. Yes, heal the mind! I was told that is impossible. We will discuss meditation; simply put meditation is slowing the mind. By sitting in a quiet place and using the techniques to focus the mind, the mind can actually stop controlling you.

"The mind is a dangerous master, but the perfect servant."
—Unknown Author

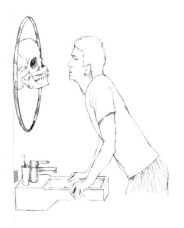

One of the most difficult parts of meditation is the feeling of "I am not doing this right". Let that go and simply enjoy. Fake it until you make it, comes to mind. If it makes you feel good, then you are doing it right. Who cares what other people say is right? They are not inside your head; they did not chew the same ground. Just trying to use the audio recording is right. Over time you will seek more answers when your mind is not so full and distracted. Then the later chapters come into play. Another major challenge is you not being hard on you. It has taken 20-30 years and in some cases a lifetime for the masters to achieve a moment of silencing the mind.

Through Mind Nidra you can feel what the masters feel when they are quieting the mind. This method is a proven shortcut on how to stop the wheel from spinning.

FACT: Since 2016, I have seen firsthand how Mind Nidra is changing lives. Seeing fellow vets come to class on day one, then watching the transformation into this new person is truly amazing. They are now able to control this anger, move beyond their past, and have a positive outlook on life.

Imagine just for a second what it would be like to shut your mind down and just be. That little window of peace is within your grasp. All I ask is that you open your mind to what I will tell you. I know this works; I have taught many other veterans and I have seen the results. They are coming off their meds, not taking their own lives, finding peace and quiet and learning how to be happy. Once you find your peace, you will be able to draw from it and calm yourself in tough situations. I know, I deal with the same challenges you face now, I was the original patient and now I want to help you through this challenging time.

Monkey Mind: Now let's look to expand on why we do what we do. The Monkey Mind is when our minds hop from subject to subject. We feel there is no "off" switch. This to me was maddening! I would try to focus, but I would lose that focus and the next thing I know I am thinking about crap I did not want to relive. Monkey Mind consumed my days; I was not happy on any one topic, yet I would hop to everything under the sun. This was one of my biggest challenges, I felt like a passenger on a nonstop flight. The pilot was doing as they liked and all I could do was take it. That took so much energy out of me, to be dragged from subject to subject. For some relief from Monkey Mind, our first step is to understand you are not alone, this is very common for all humans. When Monkey Mind was explained to me, I felt better just knowing I am not the only screwed up one with this issue. Next is acknowledgement, telling yourself that how you are behaving is an issue, will help you move towards a healthier path. The Monkey Mind sucks, but it can be controlled. For more on overcoming Monkey Mind, see Chapter 5 under "Overcoming the Monkey Mind".

Spokes in the Wheel: When we were kids, we would put baseball cards into the spokes of our bike tires. When we would ride, the cards would make clicking sounds. As we rode up and down the street, we would hear clicking. Fast forward to now. Our mind is the wheel and the events of our past are the cards. Every time our mind starts to spin, the events go clicking by. An IED, small arms fire, another patrol, the list is endless. Our wheel is spinning and like the cards these events are always there. At times it seems like there is no stopping this wheel. Can it be stopped? Can I keep going? What the hell is going on? I am strong, but this is crazy. I need help, but I am alone!

No, you are not alone; many veterans face the same challenges every day. I have created this audio recording to help you. Yes you, the one who thinks that no others know your pain. I know your pain, I lived it, I found a way out and I am now reaching my hand out to you. Seeking help is not weakness. This change is one of the strongest things you can do. Your energy may be low, you may be running on fumes, but hear me now, you can heal. What I am going to teach you is how to slow the mind and start to heal. For the first time in a long time, you will have a moment of peace. Once you achieve that peace, you will start to live a happier life.

Looking at the problems like spokes in a wheel allowed me to visualize my PTS challenges. I could, for the first time look at the bigger picture and see past all the issues. For me the issues clouded my mind (Fog) to the point I was only in that never-ending cycle. In Chapter 3 under "Anger & Identity", I outlined a method which allowed me to take a broad look at my issues. Now with the idea of spokes in the wheel, I can condense all my problems into an object. That object allows me to see many individual problems rather than one big ball of anger. Once the problems were individualized, I could start to overcome them one spoke at a time.

Allow yourself to be at peace

After teaching for a few years, I noticed veterans talked often about being peaceful or the lack thereof. I started to look inward to see if I too was holding myself back from being at peace. Speaking with veterans and hearing their stories, I realized something I never even imagined. We are not allowing ourselves to be at peace. We feel that we don't deserve peace. We traded our souls to defend our country and the cost for the survivors is spending the rest of our days in a restless state. Believing we are never allowed to be at peace is like chaining ourselves to the past. I realized I was in jail, but I held the key for the door. I, NOT ANYONE ELSE, was holding myself in prison, the prison of no peace.

Once we started to talk about this prison, we realized we all did this. We kept ourselves in peaceless prison due to our own shame, anger or lack of knowledge. Whatever the reason, we are the warden and the prisoner. I offer this, think about allowing yourself to be at peace. Just think about it, you may or may not reach that goal rapidly, but once you understand you hold the key your life will change for the better. You deserve peace no matter your past. So now I speak directly to you, the prisoner, and say search yourself for that key. It is there, you just have to look deep inside to find it. Others feel this same way and they have found their key.

The Pause: The Pause is the moment where we have that split second to either blow up or remain calm. It is that one second, we all wish we could go back to, after an ugly blow up. To pin our hopes of making the right decision within one second is not a large enough window for people with damaged brains or past traumatic events. Let's increase that window of time so we can do the right thing. We do this by looking within ourselves for early warning signs. For me I feel anger/stress and it shows up as my shoulders raised or I tighten my eyes (squinting) and my spine is arched (I get backaches). When we decide to take notice of this early warning system within our bodies, we have more time to make a rational decision, so we don't rely on that one second before a blow up. Learn your early warning signs to increase your success of practicing the pause.

How this is done- Sit somewhere comfortable. Start to relax your toes and work up to your head.

Toes, ankles, legs, hips, stomach, back, chest, hands, arms, shoulders, neck, chin, face, eyes.

For each body part you are not physically moving, just focusing on it, to check to see if it has tension. If you find tension tell that muscle to release. At first this can be a challenge, but over time it will become second nature and can be done in a supermarket line where no one can tell what you are doing. The pause will increase your time to make the right decision and not blow up. Thus, "the pause" is a continual process where we look inside for early warning signs and gain control over events in everyday life. That pause is powerful to do, and the results will speak for themselves. This is one of the tools you can use to find your path. Remember this is your path; no one can walk it for you. It is a path that at time seems lonely as others will never know you are breathing or practicing the pause, but over time loved ones and family will see the difference. You will have control.

Mind is like a Puppy: At first when you have a young puppy, it is very reckless and only wants to have fun. You take the puppy for a walk; this is new, and the puppy does not understand what is expected. Over time the puppy will learn how to act, but training it will be in small steps and take time. The same can be said about your mind. As humans, we seek fun and resist challenging times. At first meditation is like a puppy on a leash. The mind is all over the place and wants to get up and have fun. You mind will pull at its leash (your patience level). The mind does not want to sit and focus. Meditation allows you to focus and ease the issues you have. Knowing the mind is like a puppy on a leash will help you to enjoy meditation. In the beginning, you might only be capable of a few minutes, but over time, you will extend that time. You can measure your own progress by the time you can sit.

50

5 MIND NIDRA

Let's begin. What you will experience is called Mind Nidra. The word Nidra means sleep. This age-old practice aids you in focusing the mind. The first thing is to find a comfortable position. It can be sitting up, it can be lying down or whichever position is the most comfortable. Next find a quiet spot, make sure you do not have anything that can disturb you, cell phone to silent, home phone silent, close your room's door, put up a sign so everyone knows to give you some space. This is about you healing. When I say healing, I am talking about a way to heal your mind.

You may hear outside noises when you are in Mind Nidra. Acknowledge that noise (car outside, person yelling, etc.) then let it go. Letting the sound go is a major step beyond hypervigilance. We talked about hypervigilance in Chapter 2 "Fall Out". Know you are in a safe place and you are there to heal yourself. That small step of acknowledgement is your first step of living beyond your hypervigilance. As you know, being stuck in that state will drain the life out of you. Acknowledge the sound, let it go, know you are safe and reduce your hypervigilance.

Three-Part Breath: Breathing can be done standing in line, in your car or sitting down. It is your way to calm down.

One of the most powerful and portable calming exercises is the Three-Part Breath. This exercise is comprised of a full inhalation and exhalation, just breath in and out.

1. The first step is to place one hand on your stomach and the other hand on your chest.
2. Start to inhale deeply. First fill your belly completely, place gentle outward pressure on your belly to keep it expanded. Continue to inhale.
3. Start to fill your chest and continue to inhale until your shoulders start to rise slightly.
4. As you begin the exhale, the shoulders come back to a relaxed position.
5. Continue with the exhale the chest relaxes.
6. Finally draw the abdomen in towards the spine.

This exercise has a total of six steps for each breath. Remember, when you start your inhale and your belly is filled, place gentle pressure (outward with your stomach muscles) on your belly to keep it expanded. This will help once you begin your exhale portion. If there is no gentle belly pressure during your exhale, you may skip over lowering the shoulders and chest and move straight to drawing in the belly as you exhale.

Let's practice a Three-Part Breath together. Inhale into the belly (add gentle pressure), continue to inhale and expand the chest fully then when the shoulders rise; exhale, shoulders relax, chest relaxes and draw belly into your spine. Now that you understand how to do this, let's practice. Place your hands on your chest and belly. Start to inhale, filling your belly, add gentle pressure, keep inhaling and fill your chest, finally inhale until your shoulders rise slightly. Now start to exhale, letting the shoulders lower, exhale and your chest relaxes. Finally draw your belly towards your spine.

This is a great tool to use. When you are driving and someone cuts you off, make sure you are safe and then start your Three-Part Breath. If you focus on your six steps (belly, chest, shoulders, shoulders, chest, belly) then you cannot think about being mad. The faster your find your peace, the happier you will be. Anything that subtracts from your peace is too costly.

One Positive Thought: Now that you understand how to do the Three-Part Breath, it is time to move on to the next step. The next step is One Positive Thought. I can hear you now saying...

Positive? Hell, everything is negative.

Can't even think of one positive thought? I know the feeling as that was my world. To focus the mind we must have a starting point. That starting point is One Positive Thought. I cannot stress enough this is your starting point Your positive thought will allow you to begin to overcome anger, depression, etc. It is your anchor when the storm starts to rage. Your positive thought will be used during your meditation session so working through this chapter will help you later.

It can be a person, place or thing. I will give you an example then in a few seconds you will have time to find your One Positive Thought. My example is standing on the beach.

I love the beach, the wind, the sound of waves crashing, the birds overhead. To me the beach fills all my senses and I can focus. Now that you are thinking about the beach let's move forward. Just thinking about the beach is great, but it helps to use some powerful aids to help you to enjoy it more. To advance your meditation using your One Positive Thought, add in your senses. In your mind use the following to focus the mind:

You are on a beach, any beach...... now

See the beach and the horizon as far as you can see
Taste the salt on your lips,
Hear the waves crashing,
Feel the wind on your face
Smell the salt air.

What does it *feel* like? What sounds do you *hear*?
What do you *smell*? Use all your senses the best you can.

This will anchor the positive thought in your mind. I will talk about the Power of Positive later. For now take a few moments to find your positive thought.

Try to focus on one positive thing in your life. Hold that positive image in your mind's eye and never let it go. It can be a person, place, or thing; anything that brings a positive thought to you. Now working from the beach example we spoke about above let's mate that pattern (See, Taste, Hear, Feel, Smell) to your positive thought. Mold that process and make it serve you.

See the surrounding in YOUR positive thought
Hear the noises of YOUR positive thought
Feel the things nearby in YOUR positive thought
Smell the air in YOUR positive thought

This is one of your first steps towards the Power of Positive. This is also a leap of faith. Think about something that makes you happy, hold onto that thought and use it during the recording. You will hear me say "bring your mind back to your One Positive Thought" just focus on YOUR positive thought, nothing else matters. This will give your mind a point of focus.

Overcoming the Monkey Mind: A major hurdle happened when my mind wandered. When your mind wanders, and it will, try not to react negatively. By reacting negatively during meditation, I would get very mad at myself. I felt like a failure at yet another thing. I finally realized I had to be nice to me. When I would have Monkey Mind during meditation, (thoughts of paying bills, kids, job, driving here, work the next day, spouse, anger, etc.)

I would acknowledge I was not focused and refocus on my original thought. The key to meditation is One Positive Thought. Let your mind focus on that and that alone. Simply let the unwanted thought come and go away, then gently bring your attention back to your One Positive Thought.

How to focus the mind when you are meditating.

Think of it like this, you are sitting on a park bench and you are looking over a pond. The pond is peaceful and has all your attention. Then a bird flies into your view, this bird was not your focus, the pond is, but the bird now has your attention. Here is the key moment, recognize the bird has your attention then gently remind yourself that you are focused on the pond, not the bird. Allow the bird to fly away out of sight and then focus on the pond. Now bring that analogy into meditation. Don't react to the "other thought" (the bird coming into your view) simply watch the "other thought" come in and fly away. Gently bring your attention back to your One Positive Thought. Don't get upset. Just accept it and continue to practice your meditation. Let the thought come in and let them go, no reaction just refocus your mind on your One Positive Thought.

One of the biggest mistakes people make during meditation is having an expectation. We expect the mind to "focus on just one thing or have just one thought". If that does not happen then we have just failed. That failure turns us off meditation and adds another negative to our life. We were never taught how to train our mind to focus. Meditation is not about judgment it is about calming the mind. We are all too hard on ourselves.

In order to be stronger and better, we must accept we will not be perfect right away, but over time, we will be better than we were yesterday. Always bring your attention back to your One Positive Thought and it will change your life forever. Bring your One Positive Thought with you no matter where you go. For me in the beginning I spent two seconds in my positive thought and 10 seconds with Monkey Mind (bills, spouse, kids, job, etc.) I was tired of always refocusing back to my One Positive Thought. It took me a long time, but I realized I was spending equal time on the positive thought and Monkey Mind. Then it happened,

I was spending more time on my positive thought than my Monkey Mind. I made progress; it can happen, but will take time, keep at it.

6 WHAT IS COMING

Tibetan singing bowls have been around for thousands of years. They have many uses. For this audio recording I use 14 singing bowls in the recording. There will be bowls that are struck and vibrate, and bowls that are just for singing. The bowls have high and low tones. Most likely one of the bowls will resonate with you. One of the bowls will "speak to you" as the veterans say in class.

<u>Sounds of the Bowls and How to use them to Focus</u>: During meditation the mind loves to wander. Use the bowls to allow the mind to "attach" to something and help focus the mind. When the mind focuses, we can turn our energy towards relaxing the body rather than burning energy with hypervigilance. Listen for each bowl. In the beginning, you just hear the bowls, but over time you will learn to feel the bowls and the energy they produce. Strange concept, but I know firsthand, this is a real part of healing.

Use your One Positive Thought. Think of something positive and when the mind starts to wander acknowledge that your mind is wandering, don't get mad, simply refocus the mind and think about your One Positive Thought.

Start by touching toes. Before you get comfortable simply lean forward and reach for your toes. Touching your toes is not the goal. The goal is to simply round your back and stretch your back out. This is an important step for meditation. By leaning forward you are allowing the body to immediately slow down and relax. It may seem far too simple to have such a major effect. but it works. We will go in depth later in Chapter 10 "SNS vs PNS", but for now, know it is a tool to use to help you before meditation and sleep.

Hold breath and tighten your muscles. During the first 30-minute recording, you will be guided. That second half will not be words only the bowls. In the beginning, you will hear "hold your breath and tighten _____ muscle." Try to take as deep of a breath as possible and hold it. When you flex _____ muscle, flex it as hard as you can. When you hear "release" let go of both the muscle and breath, return to normal relaxed breathing and forget that body part. Let the body slowly move higher and into relaxation.

Body temperature will drop. The body truly relaxes when there is no movement and the heart slows down. When the heart slows, so does the blood flow. When the blood flow slows, the body becomes cooler. When you are in Mind Nidra, the body will cool off. You might need a blanket or something to keep you warm. You might enjoy the change in how your body feels via being cooler, your choice. This is mentioned so you are not taken by surprise by this new feeling.

Losing control over your arms and legs. At times veterans have said they felt like they lost the power to move their arms and legs during Mind Nidra. This does not happen all the time, but again you need to know what might happen. If this happens, you have options. One, take a deep breath and keep breathing deep till you can open your eyes. Two, accept this new feeling knowing this will lead you to a healthier life. We veterans have lived a certain lifestyle. We were not taught how to calm down. The lack of control over your limbs is a positive step towards relaxing the mind. All that is happening is the mind simply saying I don't need to worry about the RV (body), it is time to heal the mind (driver).

CENTER

7 C-E-N-T-E-R

Clear the mind
Even hips, straighten spine
Neutral shoulders, straighten spine
Three-Part Breath (5 deep breaths)
Evaluate yourself (how do I feel)
Release tension

Above is the overview of CENTERing. During the recording, you will hear me say, "Start to CENTER yourself." During my teacher training the instructors would say "center" yourself. I had zero clue of what they were talking about, should I sit in the center of the room? Should I think about the center of my body? I had no idea. Then I thought, "Why don't I create something that works for me?" Thus, CENTERing was born. This is the word picture of CENTERing

C "Clear the mind" If we could simply clear our minds and have them go blank, we would all be gurus and not need anything, but we are human and need some guidance. To clear the mind, start with your **eyes closed**, envision all the details of the place you are now. "See" the things that are near you, all the details you can focus on... tell yourself you are **HERE**. Next focus on the time, don't worry about the past or the future you are **NOW**.

65

You are **HERE & NOW**. I use this saying "Here & Now" many times during the day when I feel things start to spin too fast, this lets me calm down and with the Three-Part Breath I can slow the world down even if I am in a public place, no one knows I am meditating.

E "Even hips" If you are sitting or lying down this cue is designed for you to make yourself as comfortable as possible. "Clear the mind" is to relax the mind; "even hips" is to relax the body.

N "Neutral your shoulders" This is one gift you can give yourself. When we lower our shoulders, we let go of our hypervigilance and start to let the body recover. It is the gift we give ourselves.

T "Three-Part Breath" Take five deep breaths using the Three-Part Breath technique we spoke about. If you can focus on each part of each breath, you cannot stay angry.

E "Evaluate yourself" On a scale of one to ten, ask how you feel now. Give yourself an honest determination. At the end of the recorded session, you will hear "How do you feel now?" Again, compare numbers from the start to how you feel at the end.

R "Release" Without moving your body, start to scan your body to release muscle tension. Start at your toes and check to see if your toes are flexed. Then move to your feet, ankles and on up to your head.

Toes, ankles, legs, hips, stomach, back, chest, hands, arms, shoulders, neck, chin, face, eyes.

Pay attention to your shoulders. When we N, "Neutral your shoulders" did your shoulders come back up in that time? If so, you now can see that you are tense and trying to protect yourself. Allow your shoulders to come back down. The last check should be for the eyes. We hold tension in our eyes, notice that tension and let your eyes relax.

The timeframe for CENTERing should take about three minutes. Some veterans have said when they get frustrated and about to lose it, they leave the situation or wherever they are, and they sit in their vehicle. They practice CENTERing and get through the event without doing something they will regret later. It works. I use it daily to help me get past the hard times.

To listen to C-E-N-T-E-R, download the album Living Beyond PTS: Mind Nidra or the individual recordings at Spotify, Apple Music or iTunes, Amazon, Pandora, or iHeartRadio.

8 THE AUDIO RECORDINGS

The tracks: There are several options for the recordings. The "CENTERing" track is three minutes and designed to be used in the beginning before the 30-minute session. After you understand how to center yourself, you may choose not to use it in the future.

The remaining tracks are discussed below in detail and are the results of many veterans input, trust and time. We hope you enjoy the final product.

Mind Nidra Physical Practice (Meditation): Here is where we start to physically conduct the practice. All the words before this have set you up for success. You have tools to help you to meditate; you understand what anger is and where it comes from. We talked about Negative vs Positive, Monkey Mind, Spokes in a Wheel, Three-Part Breath and One Positive Thought. I know we talked about a lot of things so in the beginning use the one tool that "feels" the best to you. Later on when you want to expand your practice reread some chapters to find more tools to help you. You now have a solid base to build from. You have knowledge to grow from and most importantly should understand you are not alone in feeling the way you do.

I suggest you start with the 30-minute session as it is guided so you can simply listen and relax. Overtime you will be more open to longer sessions. That is why I created a 45-minute session and 60-minute sessions. If you have trouble sleeping at night, then you may try to use the 60-Minute Non-guided session to fall to sleep with.

30 - Minute Guided Mind Nidra: During this first session, you will be listening to a guided meditation. For this session, find a quiet place away from distractions. Let people know you will need some space and quiet. Turn off cell phones and the internet.

Find a position of comfort; sitting, lying down or however you feel comfortable. To truly get the best out of meditation the body should have no pain that will distract the mind. For some of us that is hard, but over time and through stretching you will get the body to not be in pain.

During the session, you will be asked to, "Take a deep breath and hold it." Try to fill your lungs to max and then hold. Next, you will hear "Tighten / Flex _____ muscle." Whatever muscle you are focusing on try to flex that muscle as hard as you can. When you hear "Release / Relax" let the air out and release that muscle. Then forget about that muscle, it no longer exists.

This will repeat through the entire body. Next will be "body sensing" again working from toes to head. In this part, you will not move the body, you will simply focus on a muscle and ensure it is completely relaxed. In the middle of the session, you will hear, "Bring your mind back to your

One Positive Thought." Try to focus on that only. When your mind wanders, try not to get frustrated and simply focus back on your positive thought.

In the beginning it is a challenge, but over time, you can succeed. At the end of the session, you will hear instructions on how to come back to an awakened state. After you open your eyes, sit and enjoy the feeling you have. The longer you practice the more benefits you will get. This first session may be used for months until your body and mind are open to moving to the longer sessions.

To listen to the **30 – Minute Guided Mind Nidra**, download the album Living Beyond PTS: Mind Nidra or the individual recordings at Spotify, Apple Music or iTunes, Amazon, Pandora, or iHeartRadio.

45 - Minute Guided Mind Nidra: This longer session is designed for those who are able to sit longer and feel they are ready to move forward. The actions and words are the same as the 30-minute session except you will not hear "Release / Relax". You will have the opportunity to advance through releasing on your own with the sound of the highest bowl being struck.

During the 30-minute session you would hear, "Bring your attention to your left hand, spread the fingers out, curl them into a ball, take a deep breath and hold it......... Release" (and you would let the air out and release the muscle). In this session, you will not hear release; you will focus on the words and actions and release the muscle and the air on your own. After practicing with the 30-minute session, you will know the pattern of how things go. The action of releasing on your own will draw the mind into a deeper state of meditation. You will also hear the bowls sing longer in the middle. This singing portion is where most of the veterans say they find peace.

To listen to the **45 – Minute Guided Mind Nidra**, download the album Living Beyond PTS: Mind Nidra or the individual recordings at Spotify, Apple Music or iTunes, Amazon, Pandora, or iHeartRadio.

60 - Minute Minimal Guided Mind Nidra: This session is designed for those that know the pattern and the flow of the sessions and needs less talking. During this session, you will only hear, "_____ foot." It is now on you to hold your breath, flex the muscle, and release by listening to how the bowls are being played. It is important to know the flow of Mind Nidra. As with the previous two you will be brought out by vocal directions, this 60-minute recording has minimal words to bring you out. You will notice that in the longer session, the mind truly understands how to focus and the benefits will be amazing.

To listen to the **60 – Minute Guided Mind Nidra**, download the album Living Beyond PTS: Mind Nidra or the individual recordings at Spotify, Apple Music or iTunes, Amazon, Pandora, or iHeartRadio

56 - Minute Non-Guided Mind Nidra: This session is designed to be used immediately for getting to sleep or getting back to sleep. There are no words just the sound of the bowls. The bowls will get softer and softer. You will not hear directions at the end on how to come out of it, the goal is to focus your mind so you can sleep.

To listen to the **56 – Minute Non-Guided Mind Nidra**, download the album Living Beyond PTS: Mind Nidra or the individual recordings at Spotify, Apple Music or iTunes, Amazon, Pandora, or iHeartRadio

9 AFTER MIND NIDRA

Now you have moved out of Mind Nidra. Let's look at what just happened. During Mind Nidra, your body completely shut down. You were able to focus on one thing exclusively, even if only for a moment. You achieved pinpoint focus. You were not able to think about the past or the future. You were in this moment exclusively. When your body shut down, your mind was wide-awake. This might be the first time you have ever experienced a difference between mind and body. It is close to waking from a dream when you are in that between time of awake and dreaming, but this is for an extended time. In that "Mind Nidra" time you allowed your body to shut down. The most important part is the mind is allowed to heal itself. Yes, you can fix the brain and recover from the past.

Asleep vs. Awake: During the meditation session many people say they fell asleep. At first, this is very needed and pleasant. Sleep is not something that comes easy, so when you can get it, enjoy it. The feeling people have after Mind

Nidra is one of inner peace and calmness. In the beginning when people sleep, that is a huge step forward. Over time most people start to look for a deeper experience. That searching leads them to the path of inner peace.

So far, the pillars that you learned are Anger, Monkey Mind, Spokes in The Wheel, Three-Part Breath, One Positive Thought, CENTERing and the actual practice of Mind Nidra. There is more to learn from the additional chapters. The pillars below are there to support and assist you in slowing the wheel now, and ultimately moving beyond the event.

I ask you continue to "ACT" and keep practicing. Daily practice is a key to becoming healthy. In the beginning, it may only be for minutes, but over time your meditation sessions will become longer.

House of peace, but road of challenges of anger, monkey mind and beyond:

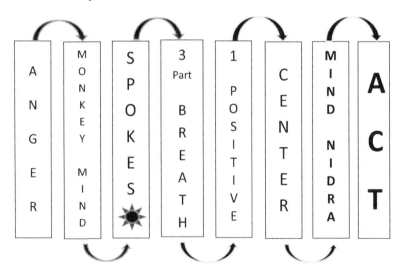

After the session: Many veterans have said after a Mind Nidra session that they saw colors or light, traveling to locations and even spoken different languages during the session. I cannot explain why this happens. What I can say is this is common and something not to be concerned about. Still other vets express concern when these events don't happen to them. My answer is simple, your body and mind are different, their path is theirs to walk and your path is yours to walk with different experiences along the way. Try not to hold yourself to a self-imposed "standard". These are just different experiences.

FACT: Separation between mind and body will happen. There will come a point where you are in that gap, where your body is asleep, and your mind is awake. That point is the separation between mind and body (RV and driver). At first, we think our mind and body are one, over time you will experience new sensations and can decide for yourself. Just know this might come up in your sessions and is something to understand and enjoy.

The Power You Now Hold: If only for a split second you now realize you have the power to stop the wheel and be at peace. At any moment, you have the ability within you to stop the noise, anxiety and tension. We have always had this within us, but we were never taught how to access it. That feeling within you now will be with you for the rest of your days, but you must keep practicing to focus the mind.

This practice is available to you whenever you need it. My goal is to help you become happy and healthy. It will not happen overnight, but it will happen. When I discovered all this I thought, "Healing slowly is better than never." The doctors seem to lack training and are running out of options in how to handle PTS. Some just want to pump us full of drugs making us a mindless drooling fool so we cannot come back into their office and bother them.

Still some doctors are looking outside the typical remedies and realizing that meditation does work. The challenge there is getting the VA to support outside ideas. Some VA hospitals do support this and some do not. Knowing there are treatments that work and require only you sit down and relax will put another tool in your toolbox.

10 GETTING TO SLEEP OR BACK TO SLEEP

Let me guess.... You wake in the night typically between 2-4 a.m.

There is a simple way to get to sleep or back to sleep. Do a forward fold, any form of forward fold. Here is what I recommend. When you are in bed swing your legs over the side and sit up on the side of your bed. Now bend at the waist and reach for your toes, you may not reach your toes and that is fine. Reaching your toes is not the goal, curving your spine is the goal.

SNS vs. PNS: Let's look at the human body for a second. Your body has a Nervous System. The two parts of the nervous system are the Central Nervous System (CNS) and the Peripheral Nervous System (PNS). The CNS is made up of the brain and spinal cord. The brain plays a major role in control of the body functions including movement, thoughts, speech, memory and awareness. The PNS connects the CNS to the limbs and organs. Within the PNS is the Sympathetic Nervous System (SNS).

OK enough medical mumbo jumbo! Here is the important part of this chapter!!!

The **Sympathetic** Nervous System keeps us on alert, it is our fight or flight response. Think back to bootcamp or basic training. You were taught to stand up straight with your head up. Those were tools we learned to help us see things and act accordingly. Those tools were used to engage our fight or flight response.

When we arch our backs, we are squeezing our adrenal glands; that pumps out adrenalin, the chemical that keeps us in fight or flight. Most veterans experience back pain, this is sometimes due to our dependency on the chemical adrenalin in our bodies. Some go to extremes to get that "rush." That rush of adrenalin we got during our time in service is now something we are addicted to.

Think of it like this, a person walks up to you in a bar with chest out and fists clinched. Just one look and you know what is coming. That person has unknowingly tapped into their sympathetic nervous system and he or she is ready to fight. With our background, we are stuck in that sympathetic nervous system; always on alert and always ready to fight.

So now the question in your mind is how do we change that?

We can change it simply by reaching for our toes and doing a forward fold. When the body does a forward fold, the opposite system comes into effect, the **Parasympathetic** Nervous System (PNS). The PNS is the opposing system of the SNS, it is designed to calm the body and relax us. It too sends out chemicals that relax us naturally.

FACT: People use drugs to alter their mind. One thing most don't know, is that our body produces more drugs than scientists can reproduce. You have a pharmacy inside of you already. Learning how to tap into that pharmacy is the key. Mind Nidra will help you move from alert to relaxed.

To access the PNS the spine must be rounded or curved. Look at it like this, when a person is afraid, they curl into the fetal position. A person so afraid they curl into the fetal position is unknowingly tapping into their PNS. This fetal position is rounding the spine and naturally sending out chemicals that relax or calm us. The body has systems to excite or calm us, but we have never been taught how to use them to our advantage.

Simply doing a forward fold and reaching for your toes or lying on your back and bringing your knees into your chest, will tap into the PNS and calm the body. The next time you cannot sleep, swing your legs over the side of your bed. Reach for your toes. Stay there for as long as your body will let you or you get sleepy.

Practice Your Three-Part Breathing;

Inhale- expand belly, expand chest, lift shoulders

Exhale- shoulders down, chest deflates, stomach deflates.

If you get dizzy during your forward fold just lay back into your bed. Understanding your body will help you move past the drugs, alcohol and sleeping pills and get real sleep.

Sleep is a challenge on many levels. Can't get to sleep, can't stay asleep and afraid of the nightmares? Some choose to self-medicate so they simply pass out. Some just don't sleep until they again pass out. Now you have another tool in your bag. Simply round your spine and learn to allow the body to shift from the SNS to the PNS. This concept blew me away. I finally realized why my back hurt. I had the power to help myself.

11 ONE POSITIVE THOUGHT

Earlier in chapter five I said I would talk more about this. Your positive thought can change your whole life. Have your positive thought ready to overcome your negative thought. Anytime a negative thought comes to mind, acknowledge the negative thought, and then bring your mind back to your positive thought. Easier said than done, I realize, but this is another step forward on your path.

With all that said above, let's talk about the rubber meeting the road. In the beginning, I could not think of One Positive Thought. EVERYTHING was negative. I would see a bird flying overhead... that was negative. I would sit down and that was negative. No matter what was going on it was negative. I was swimming in a pool of negative thoughts, actions and words. The worst part was I did not ever realize I was making everything negative. Yes, some things were negative, but I even took the positive and made it negative. Then I read this....

"When disturbed by negative thoughts, opposite (positive) ones should be thought of." – Sri Swami Satchidananda

This was the first time I really looked at how I viewed things. I started to listen to myself and I realized how negative I was. If I wanted to change, that change had to start with acknowledgement. OK step one, acknowledge I was negative. That sucked. I was not a negative person, but here I was full of negative words, actions and thoughts. Step two, find something that was positive. That was a kick in the head. I think negative, my words are negative, and my actions are negative…

Well, how do I find something positive?

One day I was reading and found a great quote.

"The pain you feel today will be the strength you will feel tomorrow." – Author Unknown

I thought, "That is positive and I will use that to shield me from the negative." During that day, I would say the positive saying as much as I could. The next morning, the fog and anger took hold again and I could not remember my positive thought. I went searching for more. I started to write these down on a piece of paper so I would not lose them. One page grew to five, that grew to 20 and still it grew. Soon I was swimming in positive sayings; all the while, I tried to think about how they applied to me and how they could help clear my mind.

One day I was talking with some vets. While we were talking, I noticed everything they were saying was negative. WOW was I just like them. I decided to share my list of the POWER OF POSITIVE (POP). We talked about how to use the POP and what it did for me. After a few weeks we talked again, and they had the same experience of POP as I did. Once we had a positive thought, we had the power to deflect the negative. I will admit in the beginning I could only focus on my positive saying for a few seconds. After time, those few seconds of positive lasted minutes. I realized in this game of positive vs. negative, I can win even if I can only hold positive for a few seconds. Over time you will expand your positive and find the one thought that will support you in times of need.

Back to that quote by Sri Swami Satchidananda, "When disturbed by negative thoughts, opposite (positive) ones should be thought of."

That simple saying has a very deep meaning to me. It shows me I do have power to control my mind. I can have a positive outlook on life. At first, it seems like only 12 words. Over time, it becomes so important it cannot be fully understood until people experience it for themselves. When we train ourselves to be positive and stop dwelling on negative everything gets better. When we see positive even in the darkest time, we can get through anything. The Power of Positive is the key.

The following is a sample of the list I have gathered and have shared with other vets. The first page gives directions on how to use it. Please take time and review at least one page. Find something that speaks to you and use it. The more you inject positive into your life the better you will feel.

12 POWER OF POSITIVE

The next pages contain many profound and positive sayings. Your entire world will change when you start to cultivate a positive outlook. When you look for positive in every breath, every step, and every event, then everything in your life will be positive.

I ask you to read the following pages. Highlight or mark the ones that resonate with you. When you need something positive in your life, pick this up and review your highlighted/marked ones. That way the power of positive will be within your grasp all the time.

When these pages become a part of your life, you can choose the statement that has helped you though the good and the bad. In the beginning, you will choose many. Over time, you will return to the list and focus on just a few. Then you will find just one statement that is your Power of Positive, which brings happiness to you no matter what you are facing. **This will be your One Positive Thought.** This statement will enable you to be positive no matter where you are or what you are facing. This One Positive statement can help calm the mind and allow you inner peace. Once you have a small piece of inner peace you are on your path to true happiness and ultimately to bliss.

Enjoy the Power of Positive.
Pass it on to others.
Anvi Shanti - Seek peace, Seek **your** peace

This section contains four pages of the quotes I like the best. At the end of the book there are additional pages of quotes. I created this to allow you to easily find positive quotes without sifting through endless pages.

ONLY POSITIVE THOUGHTS BEYOND THIS POINT

- Happiness is a choice, not a result. Nothing will make you happy until you choose to be happy. No person will make you happy unless you decide to be happy. Your happiness will not come to you. It can only come from you. – Ralph Marston

- Do not let the behavior of others destroy your inner peace. – Dalai Lama

- Your mind is a powerful thing. When you fill it with positive thoughts, your life will start to change for the good. – John Assaraf

- Weak people seek revenge. Strong people forgive. Intelligent people ignore. – Buddha

- When you truly don't care what anyone thinks of you, you have reached an awesome level of freedom. - Author Unknown

- The goal of meditation isn't to control your thoughts, it's to stop letting them control you. – Dan Millman

- Pause whenever you're about to react harshly and you'll avoid doing and saying things you'll later regret. – Lori Deschene

- The pain you feel today will be the strength you will feel tomorrow. - Author Unknown

- Practice the Pause
    - Pause before judging
    - Pause before assuming
    - Pause before accusing

- Holding on to anger is like drinking poison an expecting the other person to die. - Buddha

- There is no greater wealth in this world that Peace of mind. - Author Unknown

- Every time you are tempted to react in the same old way, ask yourself if you want to be a prisoner of the past or a pioneer of the future. – Deepak Chopra

- Stay away from negative people. They have a problem for every solution. – Albert Einstein

- Anything that costs you your peace is too expensive. - Author Unknown

- Everything happens for a reason; you provide the strength to find out why. – John Ferguson

- You cannot always control what goes on outside. But you can always control what goes on inside. – Wayne Dyer

- Do not get upset with people or situations, both are powerless without your reaction. - Buddha

- One of the best lessons you can learn in life is to master how to remain calm. – Catherine Pulsifer

- Sometimes saying sorry is the most difficult thing on earth.... But it is the cheapest thing to save the most expensive gift called a relationship. - Author Unknown

- Every time you feel yourself getting pulled into nonsense, repeat these words. "not my circus, not my monkey" - Polish Proverb

- Haters don't really hate you. They hate themselves because you are a reflection of what they wish to be. - Author Unknown

- It always seems impossible until it is done. – Nelson Mandela

- Sometimes when you are in a dark place, you think you have been buried, but you have actually been planted. – Christine Caine

- The true hero is one who conquers their own anger and hatred. – Dalai Lama

- I never lose. Either I win or I learn. – Nelson Mandela

- Inner peace begins the moment you choose not to allow another person or event to control your emotions. – Pema Chodron

- Before getting upset always ask yourself: will this even matter in the next 6 months, in a year, or in 5 years? If the answer is no, JUST LET IT GO. - Author Unknown

- Forgiveness does not change the past. It changes your future. – Bernard Meltzer

- Self-control is strength. Right thought is mastery. Calmness is power. – James Allen

- Like me or hate me both are in my favor. If you like me I am in your heart. If you hate me then I am in your mind. – William Shakespeare

- Whoever is trying to bring you down is already below you. – Ziad K Abdelnour

- You do not become good by trying to be good, but by finding the goodness that is already within you, and allowing that goodness to emerge. – Eckhart Tolle

- Before you try to change others, just remember how hard it is to change yourself. - Author Unknown

- Pain is inevitable; suffering is optional. – Haruki Murakami

- One day it just clicks... you realize what's important and what is not. You learn to care less what other people think about you and more about what you think of yourself. You realize how far you've come, and you remember when you thought things were such a mess that you would never recover. And you smile. You smile because you are truly proud of yourself and the person you've fought to become. - Author Unknown

- Silence is the best reply to a fool. - Author Unknown

- Try to make at least 3 people smile every day, beginning with you. - Author Unknown

- Anger doesn't solve anything. It builds nothing, but it can destroy EVERYTHING. – Thomas S Monson

The Warrior Section

- To hold it together when everyone else would understand if you fell apart, that's true strength. – Miyamoto Musashi

- There is nothing outside of yourself that can ever enable you to get better, stronger, richer, quicker, or smarter. Everything is within. – Miyamoto Musashi

- But where life is more terrible that death, it is then the truest valor to dare to live. – Inazo Nitobe (Author of Bushido)

- Truth is not what you want it to be; it is what it is and you must bend to its power or live a lie. – Miyamoto Musashi

- With the right attitude, self-imposed limitations vanish. – Alexander the Great

- The happiness of your life depends on the quality of your thoughts. – Marcus Aurelius, Roman emperor

- The best answer to anger is silence- Marcus Aurelius

- How much more grievous are the consequences of anger than the causes of it. – Marcus Aurelius

- You have power over your mind- not outside events. Realize this and you will find strength. – Marcus Aurelius

- I never lose. Either I win or I learn. – Nelson Mandela

- Do not pray for an easy life. Pray for the strength to endure a difficult one. – Bruce Lee

- All men die, but not all men really live. – William Wallace

- Yesterday was my day to die. Today is my day to live. – John Ferguson

At the end of the book are more pages to review. I see new perspectives on things as I read these quotes. The quotes are very helpful and I can expand my mind. I hope you take the time to review "More P.O.P" at the end of the book.

$10 Story: Imagine there are two people facing each other. Person One has $10 in their hand. Person Two has nothing. Person One with the $10 has two things: they have money and they are happy because of the money. Person two has no money and is unhappy.

Person two, with no money, takes the $10 bill from the first person. In that split second two things happen. The money changes hands, but a slightly more important issue happens. The happiness also changes hands. Yes, money is a necessary part of our culture.

The focus of this story is not the taking of money it is taking of happiness. Now let's replace the term money and focus on happiness.

When another person tries to take your happiness away via harsh words, threats or whatever; you have the power to **not** allow your happiness to be taken. That other person is suffering so much they need to try to take your happiness away to make themselves happy.

You can simply ignore them and walk away. My challenge in life is trying to help that other person, which is not my usually instinct.

Taking that story one step further, are you the victim or are you the thief from the story? If you are the victim you can start to realize what is going on and protect yourself. If you are the thief trying to steal happiness because you have none inside, you can use this story to realize what you are doing and start to alter your path. With knowledge we can all move towards happiness.

13 EFFECTS OF MEDITATION

One reason I was drawn to meditation was that the Samurai practiced it. To me, they are one of the finest warriors to walk the earth. Why would these elite fighters practice something useless? They would not. Meditation is the art of focusing the mind. It is a strange concept to control our mind, but we can. By this point you may have experienced the 30-minute recording. If so, you have experienced something and want to reach higher levels of personal growth. The want you feel is the desire to heal.

Mind Nidra is not sleep; it llows a person to utilize the potential that is lost in sleep. When we are awake our body does minimal repairing of the mind, since the energy is being used for movement, speech, etc. When a person sleeps, they shut off some of their senses as their brain goes to work fixing itself. In this sleep state (Light, REM, Deep) your mind is processing, but your body is shut off. It is that fine line we need to pursue.

The stage between being completely awake and completely asleep is the key!

The state of the body totally releasing, coupled with the mind being wide-awake, is what meditation is about. It is this completely new and amazing state where our body doesn't exist. While you don't care about your body at that moment, the mind is awake (as though we are talking with someone). This state is important for your path to healing. We think of ourselves as just our body. The mind is simply a part of the body. Through Mind Nidra you will learn they are two separate things and are controlled differently.

For me, this opened a completely new world. I was able to think like normal, but could not move my body. My arms at first were heavy then after some time they just seemed to disappear. The deeper I meditated the more of my body would disappear. I knew my body was still attached, but I chose to flow down this new path. Then I realized I was not in pain.

My body was asleep, but I was thinking like normal. This to me was amazing and scary all at the same time. I continued playing with this feeling and realized when I was done, my body was not in pain and my mind was clearer. WOW! The doctors told me they could do nothing for me, but by meditating I discovered how to 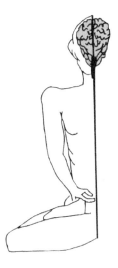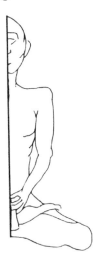 help myself. Through Mind Nidra, once our body is shut off, the mind starts to heal on its own terms. That is neuroplasticity. Your body recreates new neural highways. Those new highways allow your mind to operate better, access memories and retrain to live a healthy life.

Through neuroplasticity your mind regrows neurological pathways, repairs damages of Traumatic Brain Injuries (TBI) and you can think more clearly. This is my experience and other veterans have said the same thing.

First, you must be open to change, a change so profound that just to speak of the outcome sounds too good to be true. Heal your mind...

It is possible!!

During Mind Nidra, your mind goes beyond healing the physical body and into unchartered territory. The mind is freed to heal itself, not on a physical level, but on a neurological level. Through Mind Nidra, neurons begin to reconnect. Mind Nidra allows a person to access segments of the brain that we, in our normal wakened state or in sleep, can never access.

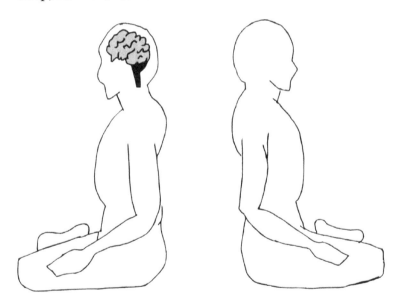

Potential of sleep is lost on the unopened and unaware mind. Once opened and aware, the mind can accept the fact healing is inherently within us and we begin the journey to heal. While awake, you are connected to your senses and thus unreceptive to healing. During Mind

Nidra, you are receptive to healing.

One of the most rewarding parts of teaching other veterans are the stories at the end. They tell me stories about missions or patrols with tears in their eyes and they tell me that they "let it go". They are accessing parts of their brain they shut off and now are moving past the hurt and moving forward with healing.

Good vs. Bad: In the beginning, Mind Nidra is a great tool to relax the body and mind. There is no standard time frame for healing, but there is a flow to it.

1st phase - The body is learning how to relax, moving away from hypervigilance. Mind Nidra is effortless and a positive experience. Most tell me they feel no aches or pain during meditation. Feeling no pain is usually only achieved after taking powerful medications. Now by sitting down and relaxing they find they have the power to release pain and feel better. This phase is mostly involving the body. Some veterans are able to let the mind open and relax, but mostly this is about the body.

2nd phase - Once the body "learns" how to release and relax, then Mind Nidra shifts to focusing on the mind. Phase two is difficult as the mind now says, "My turn to relax." Mind Nidra takes a sharp downturn. Here is where your resolve must come into play and keep you going.

Phase one was great as the body let go. In phase two, the mind wants its turn to release, so your meditation sessions will become more difficult. Knowing that difficulty may arise will help you to overcome this obstacle. Some may experience different sensations or emotions, but this is the pattern most veterans tell me about. In order to overcome this obstacle, we need to break away from the explanation of phases and revisit our "closet" we marked do not open.

Dealing with the closet marked "Never Open"

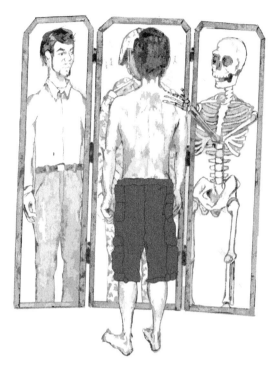

FACT: Most of us put our bad memories in a closet, marked "never open." We stick more crap in there with no intention of opening it. For me, I was afraid to open my closet and have 12 memories all screaming at me all at the same time. The idea of that intense conflict kept my door locked tight. Then a friend asked me a question. He said, "Tell me what you don't want to tell me." That hit like a ton of bricks, "I will not tell you that, I can't even admit it to myself." It was at that point I finally admitted to myself that I have things hidden away. I discovered I had a closet. With more thought I discovered it was marked never open. That took some weight off my shoulders, but it also showed me I had more work to do. Before knowing I had a closet I was convinced I had issues, but could not place my finger on what it is. Now knowing about my closet, I could see things more clearly.

Knowing about the closet and opening the closet were two completely different things. I lived with that knowledge for years, but it nagged at me. I finally decided I needed to deal with that closet, but how? Another friend gave me this idea of how to deal with the closet and I share it with you now.

THE ANSWER – I have one rule **GET IN LINE**. Too simple? I thought so at first. I still use this now and will keep on until my closet is empty.

I will open my closet; the memories or events will form a line and I invite the first memory to sit and talk. I will think about that memory, reason with that memory and over time (days, weeks or even longer) that memory will get up and walk away. Holding to my word, I will sit down with the next memory and will keep going until there is no line.

THE ESCAPE CLAUSE – You have the power to close that closet at any time. If those memories don't line up and you cannot address just one, close the door. In time, go back when you are stronger and apply the same rule. Get in line, address the first one, let it leave and then move on.

Remember Rule One - **GET IN LINE**.

3rd phase - Using the get in line method, the mind slowly frees up from all the memories that drag us down. Mind Nidra revolves back to an effortless and positive experience as it was in the beginning. As the mind dumps its painful memories, it is able to tap into past happy memories that we thought were lost. This is where neuroplasticity is coming into play.

Other veterans have told me they are able to think more clearly, they can focus better. This is due to the body's ability to "rewire" itself. Yes, the brain can fix itself, but you have to allow it to slow down and heal. Mind Nidra does that. Think of Mind Nidra like this, you have your internet browser open and many tabs open. Some are operating, some are frozen, your computer is trying to keep up, but the performance is poor.

Now what happens if you close some tabs? You get down to one tab and the computer works properly. That is what happens in Mind Nidra, you relax the body, then the mind. You address old issues and slowly you notice you are not angry so often. You actually smile and feel good for a time. There will be days where you slide back, but now it is two steps forward and only one back. You have traction and a path to being healthy. Mind Nidra will guide you there.

14 NEXT STEP

Moving further into your practice here are a few suggestions. To assist you in focusing the mind try to place your hands together. During the session, you will hear, "If you need to make any adjustment to make yourself five percent more comfortable go ahead and do that."

<u>Hands and thumbs together:</u> Bring your hands together. More importantly try not to use muscles to keep your hands together, just let them come together. Place your thumbs together. Notice the pulse in your thumbs. Bring all your attention to your pulse. Feel the heart pushing your blood through the arteries and veins. Let this rhythmic beat draw all your attention. You might think this will take away from your One Positive Thought.

At times, a positive thought may escape us, so this is "Plan B." Let the pulse between your thumbs be your point of focus. Over time you will be able to feel your pulse in other parts of your body. This will happen after you have learned what your pulse feels like in your thumbs. Again, this can be another stone to build upon. When you are frustrated you will have the power to stop think and feel your pulse. When you notice that your pulse is elevated, you know how to slow it down through the Three-Part Breath.

<u>I-O-N Breath:</u> Another step forward is the ION breath. The same steps are taken, as in the Three-Part Breath, but now we add in more. ION's are part of an atom. They can be

negative or positive. ION breath helps us focus the mind in a new way.

I - Breathe **I**n. Inhale for a count of four (thousand 1, thousand 2, etc.)

O-Breath **O**ut. Exhale for a count of eight (double the inhale time)

N- **N**eutral. This is the natural pause we all have between breaths. It is during this natural pause we can relax a muscle. For a count of four, focus on a muscle of your choice and let it relax.

Simply replace the Three-Part Breath with the ION breath. Both are the same, but the ION includes a count for each part and focuses on relaxing a muscle. Over time, the lengths can increase. The exhale or the breath out is twice as long as the inhale.

<u>Altering Body Temperature:</u> Yes you can alter your body temperature. Think about it, when you are sick your body changes its temperature all by itself. During your session, you will hear, "You may choose a warm or a cool feeling." You get to choose warm or cool, but you can also choose hot or cold. Focus all the attention on a cold (or hot) place, such as winter in Alaska. Feel the cold breeze on your feet, breathe in the freezing air; see the snow all around you. Use every sense you have to feel the cold. Over time you will feel cooler. You can adjust your own body temperature. This is a goal down the road, but it is possible.

15 **CLOSING**

This book is dedicated to those who suffer like I do. Also, to let you know there is a way out with no medications to take or negative habits that will do more damage than good. We are in the repeating pattern of injured veterans, but this is our time to break that cycle.

With knowledge and support we can heal, regain a healthy life and ensure the next generation has the key to understanding how to recover. We few who chose to defend our flag suffer silently. This suffering was a mysterious beast, but this beast's days are numbered as our country's veterans draw strength from knowledge and peace from practice.

No matter the timeframe we served, the results have been the same. Pain and anger. We continue to be handled the same, whether WWII, Korea, Vietnam or Iraq/Afghanistan. One of the major challenges is the VA just does not understand the issues of war we face.

One of the major complaints I hear from other vets is the over prescribing of medications. I too was handled this way; I was told I needed powerful medications. The veterans in my classes are tired of taking a handful of meds during the day. Some medications make us "feel out of it" and "detached" to the point we do not feel pain. We simply don't feel anything.

For some that is needed, but for most, it is not. I add this so you know how others feel. You can make the decision for yourself about how you are being handled.

Veterans' Stories

Bill - Vietnam Veteran, USMC:
My first yoga class was the result of searching for new ways
to combat stress. I viewed yoga with skepticism, so I
convinced myself that if nothing else I would at least get
some additional exercise. I had nothing to lose, so I gave
yoga a try. The class was interesting and informative. The
stretching was great, but somewhat difficult. I began using
muscles I never realized I had. The yoga Nidra portion of
the class was an entirely new experience.
   I left the class feeling a little sore and somewhat
different which I cannot describe. The following day I
began to feel a little calmer. I began attending yoga class
on a regular basis. My stretching and balance improved
which enhanced my mobility. The yoga Nidra sessions
provided me with a sense of calmness and emotional
wellbeing. I walk several miles every day for exercise. I
suffer from arthritis in my lower back, which causes pain
while walking. One day I tried a squatting pose I learned in
John's class. I remained in the squatting pose for several
minutes then proceeded with my walk. I suddenly realized
the pain in my lower back was no longer present. I felt I
had just given my body the command, "Heal thyself". You
have nothing to lose by trying yoga for physical and
emotional wellbeing; it is only when you fail to try yoga
that you lose.

Mike - Army Veteran:
Yoga for Vets and YOU have made such a positive impact
on my life ... perhaps when I needed it the most ... retired
from the Army after 37+ years, and now (retired, retired!!)
I look so forward to every Wednesday evening ... to address
and enhance my overall well being physically, mentally,

and emotionally!! The shared camaraderie with fellow Veterans and their Spouses through Yoga and Yoga Nidra is a very special experience ... THANK YOU!!

Dom - Vietnam Veteran, Navy:
I know in my case; your yoga sessions have given me the knowledge and have showed me the way to help give me clarity of the mind. It has given me awareness to what is happening in the moment, that helps reduce my anxiety caused by PTSD, by doing yoga it calms the body and thoughts that you experience and reduces the intensity. Yoga gives my mind a calming effect and allows my mind to allow bad thoughts and sensations to pass. This will help you get a deeper level of relaxation and to feel peace within, it provides a must needed soothing effect. Since coming to your classes with repeated practice and guidance from you it has provided me with relief and a fresh perspective from PTSD. Thank you.

Andy - Vietnam Veteran, USA:
I want to take this opportunity to thank you for donating your time teaching my fellow Veterans and me the techniques of YOGA and how to relax. I appreciate very much what you have done for us. I think I am in a better place thanks to you and YOGA. Some of the changes that I have made in my life and the positive affects regarding your YOGA training are as follows:

My Wife has informed me that I am more relaxed when I come home on Friday mornings after YOGA class. YOGA for me is very therapeutic in a very positive way.

I think that YOGA calms me down. I definitely feel as though I am in a better place during YOGA. The breathing exercises that you have taught me have helped me to forget my problems and to relax. During YOGA, I seem to forget about most of my aches and pains. I have lots of aches and pains! I feel that I can better deal with the realities of everyday stress. I can let things go that are bothering me. I believe that I can now better deal with my traumatic experiences. I have seen how you have also helped some of my Veteran friends that I used to think would never forgive and forget about their traumatic experiences, but that are more relaxed now due to your YOGA classes. There will be more Vets joining our classes soon. All of the Veterans with PTSD should attend your classes. Thanks again John for all that you do. I certainly appreciate your genuine caring and professionalism in sharing your knowledge of YOGA with us.

Summing up the Book: The Following is Your Guide:

Accept this is possible
Understand we all use our primal state.
Acknowledge / Knowledge / Act
The Fog
The Monkey Mind
The Spokes in the Wheel

Tools to help you overcome:

The Pause
Three-Part Breath
Power of Positive
SNS vs. PNS
CENTER
PHYSICAL PRACTICE ***DAILY***
 (30-45-60 minute recordings)

"The final stage of healing is using what happened to you to help other people" – Gloria Steinem

More Power of Positive to Consider

- Don't worry if people don't like you. Most people are struggling to like themselves--- Karen Salmansohn

- Never lie to someone who trusts you and never trust someone who lies to you. – Deanna Wadsworth

- Finish each day and be done with it. You have done what you could. Tomorrow is a new day. – Ralph Waldo Emerson

- Talk about your blessings more than you talk about your problems. - Author Unknown

- There is no enemy outside our soul. The real enemies live inside us: Anger, Ego, Geed and Hate. - Author Unknown

- Happiness is a choice, not a result. Nothing will make you happy until you choose to be happy. No person will make you happy unless you decide to be happy. Your happiness will not come to you. It can only come from you. – Ralph Marston

- Do not let the behavior of others destroy your inner peace. – Dalai Lama

- Your mind is a powerful thing. When you fill it with positive thoughts, your life will start to change for the good. – John Assaraf

- The best revenge is always to just happily move on and let Karma do the rest. - Author Unknown

- Stress makes you believe that everything needs to happen right now. Faith assures you that everything will happen at the right and perfect time. - Author Unknown

- Buddha was asked what he gained from meditation. He answered "nothing, but let me tell you what I have lost: Anger, anxiety, insecurity, depression, fear of old age and death".

- If someone treats you badly, just remember there is something wrong with them, not you. Normal people don't hurt other human beings. - Author Unknown

- Life is the most difficult exam. Many people fail because they try to copy others, not realizing that everyone has a different question paper. - Author Unknown

- Suffering is not holding you; you are holding suffering. - Buddha

- Be a Warrior, not a Worrier. – Elizabeth Archer

- When you truly don't care what anyone thinks of you, you have reached an awesome level of freedom. - Author Unknown

- The goal of meditation isn't to control your thoughts, it's to stop letting them control you. – Dan Millman/Ajay Puri/Ashit Dave

- I lost myself trying to please everyone. Now I am losing everyone as I find myself. - Author Unknown

- Happy are those who take life day by day, complaining very little, and are thankful for the little things in life. - Author Unknown

- The pain you feel today will be the strength you will feel tomorrow. - Author Unknown

- If you cannot find peace within yourself, you will never find it anywhere else. – Marvin Gaye

- When you look for the good in others, you discover the good in yourself. – Martin Walsh

- Surround yourself with people who make you a better person. - Author Unknown

- Do good for others. It will come back in unexpected ways. – Karen Salmansohn

- Silence is the best answer to someone who doesn't value your words. - Author Unknown

- Remember when you forgive, you heal. When you let go, you grow. - Author Unknown

- The less you respond to rude, critical, argumentative people, the more peaceful your life will become. – Mandy Hale

- One positive thought can change your day. So, a positive attitude can change your whole life. - Author Unknown

- You'll never be happy, if you continue to hold on to the things that make you sad. - Author Unknown

- Before you speak "THINK"   - Author Unknown
  - T= is it True
  - H= is it Helpful
  - I= is it Inspiring
  - N= is it Necessary
  - K= is it Kind

- The things that hurt you, actually teach you some of the best lesson in life. - Author Unknown

- Surround yourself with people who: Empower you. Believe in you. Support you. Uplift you. Motivate you. Appreciate you. - Author Unknown

- If it comes, let it. If it goes, let it. Don't hold onto things, and you'll find peace. - Author Unknown

- Your beliefs don't make you a better person, your behavior does. – Sukhraj S Dhillon

- The best 6 doctors: – Wayne Fields
  - Sunshine
  - Water
  - Rest
  - Air
  - Exercise
  - Diet.

- When you're wrong admit it. When you are right be quiet. – Ogden Nash

- A mistake which makes you Humble is much better than an achievement that makes you Arrogant. - Author Unknown

- Relationships are not an exam to pass or fail and not a competition to win or lose, but it's a feeling in which you care for someone more that yourself. - Author Unknown

- Before you speak, let your words pass through three gates. Is it true? Is it Necessary? Is it Kind? - RUMI

- 7 rules for a happy marriage - Author Unknown
  - Never both be angry at the same time.
  - Never yell at each other
  - Let your partner win the argument.
  - If you criticize, do it lovingly
  - Never bring up past mistakes.
  - Don't neglect each other
  - Never go to sleep with an argument unsettled.

- When your passion and purpose is greater that your fears and excuses, you will find a way. – Nishan Panwar

- Happiness starts with you. Not with your relationships, not with your job, not with your money, but with YOU. – Mandy Hale

- 5 tips for a happy life. - Author Unknown
  - Love yourself
  - Do good
  - Always forgive
  - Harm no one
  - Be positive

- My day begins and ends with gratitude and joy. – Louise Hay

- Practice the Pause
  - Pause before judging
  - Pause before assuming
  - Pause before accusing

- Pause whenever you're about to react harshly and you'll avoid doing and saying things you'll later regret. – Lori Deschene

- Every thought we think is creating our future. – Louise Hay

- When you wish good for others, good things come back to you. This is the law of nature. – Buddha

- Don't believe everything you think. – Jenny Bogart

- 10 signs you are doing well in life.   - Author Unknown
  - You have a roof over your head
  - You ate today
  - You have a good heart
  - You wish good for others.
  - You have clean water
  - Someone cares for you.
  - You strive to be better
  - You have clean clothes
  - You have a goal
  - You are alive

- Beautiful things happen when you distance yourself from negativity. - Author Unknown

- Do not get upset with people or situations, both are powerless without your reaction. - Buddha

- 7 important rules in life.   - Author Unknown
    - Make peace with your past so it won't disturb your present.
    - What other people think of you is none of your business.
    - Time heals almost everything. Give it time
    - No one is in charge of your happiness, except YOU.
    - Don't compare your life to others and don't judge them. You have no idea what their journey is all about.
    - Stop thinking too much. It's alright not to know the answer. They will come to you when you least expect it.
    - Smile, you don't own all the problems in the world.

- There are 2 ways to be happy, Change the situation, or change your mindset towards it. – Robert Tew

- Life is an echo, what you send out comes back. What you sow you reap. What you give you get. What you see in others exists in you. Remember life is an echo. It always gets back to you. So give goodness. – Chinese Proverb

- A Frog decided to climb to the top of the tree. All the frogs shouted, "it's impossible". Still the frog reached the top of the tree. How? Because the frog was deaf. The frog thought everyone was encouraging him to reach the top. "be deaf to negative thoughts" - Author Unknown

- One lie can ruin a thousand truths. – Ghanaian Proverb

123

- Every time you are tempted to react in the same old way, ask yourself if you want to be a prisoner of the past or a pioneer of the future. – Deepak Chopra

- Never be controlling by 3 things. - Author Unknown
    o Your past
    o Money
    o People

- Don't change yourself to win someone's heart. Stay true and you'll find someone who likes you for being you. – Jessica Gilbert

- The word "spiritual" really means to "search for" "to investigate" the true nature of the mind. There's nothing spiritual outside. Spiritual means the mind and spiritual people are those who seek its nature. - Author Unknown

- Stay away from negative people. They have a problem for every solution. – Albert Einstein

- The worst distance between 2 people is misunderstanding. – Yash Patel

- If you are depressed, you are living in the past. If you are anxious, you are living in the future. If you are at peace, you are living in the present. – Lao Tzu

- I respect people who tell me truth, no matter how hard it is. - Author Unknown

- Anything that costs you your peace is too expensive. - Author Unknown

124

- Nothing happens by chance. Everything has meaning. Please be convinced that your inner life is already endowed with everything you need. No matter how difficult your situation may be, you are alive now, and there is no treasure more precious that life itself. – Daisaku Ikeda

- Forgive others, not because they deserve forgiveness, but because you deserve peace. – Jonathan Lockwood Huie

- Karma! Think good thoughts, say nice things, do good for others. Everything comes back. - Author Unknown

- Everything happens for a reason; you provide the strength to find out why. – John Ferguson

- Great minds discuss ideas. Average minds discuss events. Small minds discuss people. – Eleanor Roosevelt

- Be selective in your battles. Sometimes peace is better than being right. - Author Unknown

- Don't waste your time with explanations. People only hear what they want to hear. – Paulo Coelho

- What you think- you become. What you feel- You attract. What you imagine- you create. - Buddha

- All that we are is a result of what we have thought. The mind is everything. What we think we become. - Buddha

- Energy flows where attention goes. - Author Unknown

- What comes easy won't last. What lasts won't come easy. – Ben Francia

- You cannot always control what goes on outside. But you can always control what goes on inside. – Wayne Dyer

- It takes COURAGE to let something go than it does to hang on to it, trying to make it better. Letting go doesn't mean accepting what is, exactly as it is, without fear, resistance, or a struggle for control. -Iyana Vansant

- Life is not about being rich, being popular, being highly educated, or being perfect. It is about being real, being humble and being kind. - Author Unknown

- Experience is the hardest teacher. It gives you the test first and the lesson afterwards. – Oscar Wilde

- In life you will realize there is a role for everyone you meet. Some will test you; some will use you; some will love you, and some will teach you. But the ones who are truly important are the ones who bring out the best in you. They are the rare and amazing people who remind you why it's worth it. - Author Unknown

- The root of all suffering is attachment. - Buddha

- There is no path to happiness, happiness is the path. – Buddha

- Religion is following the messenger. Spirituality is following the message. – Priya Velichala

- First they ignore you, then they laugh at you, then they fight you, then you win. – Mahatma Gandhi

- If you believe it will work out, you'll see opportunities. If you believe it won't you will see obstacles. – Wayne Dyer

- Among the things you can give and still keep are.... Your word, a smile and a grateful heart. – Zig Ziglar

- One of the best lessons you can learn in life is to master how to remain calm. – Catherine Pulsifer

- If you don't try to stop whatever is going on in your mind, but merely observe it, eventually you'll begin to feel a tremendous sense of relaxation and openness. --- Mingur Rinpoche

- Sometimes saying sorry is the most difficult thing on earth.... But it is the cheapest thing to save the most expensive gift called a relationship. - Author Unknown

- Your mind is a magnet: If you always think of positive, you attract more positive. If you always think of problems, you attract more problems. Always keep good thoughts and always stay positive. – Shanmithd Chandrasekoran

- The secret of living well and longer: eat half, walk double, laugh triple and love without measure. – Tibetan Proverb

- When you live in complete acceptance of what is, that is the end of all drama in your life. – Eckhart Tolle

- Every time you feel yourself getting pulled into nonsense, repeat these words. "not my circus, not my monkey"- - Polish Proverb

- Silence is sometimes the best answer. – Dalai Lama

- Think positive, be positive- Author Unknown

- Some people come in your life as a blessing; others come in your life as lessons. – Mother Teresa

- Whatever the present moment contains, accept it as if you had chosen it. – Eckhart Tolle

- When it hurts observe. Life is trying to teach you something. – Anita Krizzan

- No poison can kill a positive thinker; no medicine can save a negative thinker. - Author Unknown

- Never blame anyone for your life. Good people give you happiness. Bad people give you experience. Worst people give you lessons. Best people give you memories. - Author Unknown

- When ego comes, everything else goes. When ego goes, everything else comes. – Sudhanshu Rane

- The biggest communication problem is that we do not listen to understand we listen to reply. – Stephen R Covey

- Maturity comes when you stop making excuses and start making changes. - Author Unknown

- Haters don't really hate you. They hate themselves because you are a reflection of what they wish to be. - Author Unknown

- To be happy you must: - Author Unknown
  - Let go of what's gone
  - Be grateful for what remains
  - Look forward to what's coming next.

- 5 things to quit right now: - Author Unknown
  - Trying to please everyone
  - Fearing change
  - Living in the past
  - Putting yourself down
  - Overthinking

- Note to self: - Buddha
  - Keep trying
  - Be good
  - Stay positive
  - Be awesome
  - Become better…. Not better than anyone else, but better than the person you were yesterday.

- It always seems impossible until it is done. – Nelson Mandela

- How people treat you is their KARMA. How you react to it is yours. – Wayne Dyer

- Peace begins when the expectation ends. – Sri Chinmoy

- I do not fix my problems. I fix my thinking. The problems fix themselves. – Louise Hay

- What's meant for you will never pass you by. - Author Unknown

- Feelings are just visitors. Let them come and go. Don't get attached to them. - Mooji

- Sometimes when you are in a dark place, you think you have been buried, but you have actually been planted. – Christine Caine

- Dear past than you for the lesson. Dear future, I am ready. - Author Unknown

- If people say something bad about you, judge you as if they know you, don't feel bad just remember "dogs bark if they don't know the person" - Author Unknown

- True love is when you are happy spending time together. - Author Unknown

- If you are helping someone and expecting something in return, you are doing business not kindness. - Author Unknown

- You live most of your life inside your head. Make sure it is a nice place to be. - Buddha

- Minding your business eliminates half the problems in your life. - Author Unknown

- If you just watch things, just sit still and let the world exist in front of you – just for a second time freezes and the world pauses and if you somehow found a way to live in that second, then you would live forever. – Lauren Oliver

- No anger inside means no enemy outside. – Deepika G

- Sometimes I just look up, Smile, and say "I know that was you". - Author Unknown

- When thinking about life, remember this: No amount of guilt can solve the past, and no amount of anxiety can change the future. - Author Unknown

- TRUST is one word. One second to say. One lifetime to prove it. - Author Unknown

- Here is a basic truth: to do anything, we must first believe it can be done. – David J Schwartz

- 5 things to do before you get out of bed in the morning: - Author Unknown
    o Express gratitude
    o Set your intentions for the day
    o Take five long deep breaths in and out
    o Smile for no reason
    o Forgive yourself for yesterday's mistakes

- Satisfied life is better that successful life. Because our success is measured by others. But our satisfaction is measured by our own soul, mind and heart. - Author Unknown

- Before getting upset always ask yourself: will this even matter in the next 6 months, in a year, or in 5 years? If the answer is no, JUST LET IT GO. - Author Unknown

- Maturity is learning to walk away from people and situations that threaten your peace of mind, self-respect, values, morals and self-worth. - Author Unknown

- Letting go doesn't mean that you don't care about someone anymore. It is just realizing that the only person you really have control over is yourself. – Deborah Reber

- Forgiveness does not change the past. It changes your future. – Bernard Meltzer

- 7 steps to happiness: - Author Unknown
    o Think less, feel more
    o Frown less, Smile more
    o Talk less, Listen more
    o Judge less, Accept more
    o Watch less, do more
    o Complain less, appreciate more
    o Fear less, Love more

- Think of non-thinking. - Author Unknown

- One moment of pure awareness is one moment of perfect enlightenment. - Author Unknown

- Freedom comes when you stop caring about what others think of you. – Yashika Oberoi

- Holding onto anger is like drinking poison and expecting the other person to die. - Buddha

- Meditation will not carry you to another world, but it will reveal the most profound and awesome dimensions of the world in which you already live. - Author Unknown

- Depression is when you don't really care about anything; Anxiety is when you care too much about everything. And having both is just like hell. - Author Unknown

- When you give and expect a return that is an investment, but when you give and expect nothing that is pure love. - Author Unknown

- Like me or hate me both are in my favor. If you like me, I am in your heart. If you hate me then I am in your mind. – William Shakespeare

- Whoever is trying to bring you down is already below you. – Ziad K Abdelnour

- Anything which is troubling you, anything which is irritating you THAT is your teacher. – Ajahn Chah

- Sometimes people pretend you are a bad person, so they don't feel guilty about the things they did to you. - Author Unknown

- If you can control your mind you can control your life. – Lao Tzu

- Accept what is, let go of what was, and have faith in what will be. - Author Unknown

- Appreciate those who love you. Help those who need you. Forgive those who hurt you. Forget those who leave you. - Author Unknown

- People talk behind your back for 3 reasons: - Author Unknown
    o When they can't reach your level.
    o When they don't have what you have.
    o When they try to copy your lifestyle, but can't.

- Silence isn't empty. It's full of answers. - Author Unknown

- Be kind, for everyone you meet is fighting a hard battle. - Philo

- The secret to happiness is not found in seeking more, but developing the capacity to enjoy less. - Socrates

- The secret to change is to focus all of your energy, not fighting the old, but on building the new. - Socrates

- The most dangerous liars are those who think they are telling the truth. - Author Unknown

- Meditation opens up a whole new world. - Author Unknown

- Find your passion and create your life based on this passion. - Author Unknown

- 4 beautiful thoughts of life.   - Author Unknown
  - Look back and get experience
  - Look forward to see hope
  - Look around and find reality.
  - Look within and find yourself.

- Do what gives you peace. - Kuldeep

- I don't care what people think or say about me, I know who I am, and I don't have to prove ANYTHING to ANYONE! - Sinu

- Sometimes you just need to focus on YOU... And that's OK. - Author Unknown

- Not everyone will understand your journey, that's okay. You're here to live your life, not to make everyone understand. - Banksy

- Breathing in, I calm body and mind. Breathing out I smile. Dwelling in the present moment I know this is the only moment. – Thich Nhat Hanh

- Being a good person does not depend on your religion, status in life, skin color, political views or culture. It depends on how you treat others. - Author Unknown

- The past has no power over the present moment. – Eckhart Tolle

- Some changes look negative on the surface, but you will soon realize that space is being created in your life for something new to emerge. - Eckhart Tolle

- The primary cause of unhappiness is never the situation, but the thoughts about it. - Eckhart Tolle

- You do not become good by trying to be good, but by finding the goodness that is already within you, and allowing that goodness to emerge. – Eckhart Tolle

- Before you try to change others, just remember how hard it is to change yourself. - Author Unknown

- Worry does not take away tomorrow's troubles. It takes away today's peace. - Author Unknown

- You cannot stop the storm, but meditation helps you find its still center. - Author Unknown

- Control your emotions or they will control you. – Chinese Proverb

- Better than a thousand hollow words, is one word that brings peace. - Buddha

- Train your mind to see the good in everything. Positivity is a choice. – Megha Bhat

- If you can stay positive in a negative situation, you win. - Author Unknown

- Fear does not stop death, it stops life. - Author Unknown

- Never argue with a fool. People watching may not be able to tell the difference. – Dr. Swapna Parker

- Pain is inevitable; suffering is optional. – Haruki Murakami

- Love is when the other person's happiness is more important than your own. – H Jackson Brown Jr

- Silence is the best reply to a fool. - Author Unknown

- Don't regret growing older. It's a privilege denied to many. – Syeda Ruba Fatima

- Stop expecting. Start accepting. Life becomes much easier. – Nikhik Sancheti

- Don't waste your life trying to impress others. - Author Unknown

- Appreciate good people. They are hard to find. – Reshu Gupta

- You will not be punished for your anger; you will be punished by your anger. - Buddha

- Enjoy the simple pleasures in your life, and never take them for granted. - Author Unknown

- Forgive everyone, including yourself for everything. - Author Unknown

- Develop equanimity in the face of daily challenges. - Author Unknown

- Get rid of anything that isn't useful, beautiful or joyful. - Author Unknown

- Enjoy the journey of your life. There are no endpoints, just turning points. - Author Unknown

- Try to make at least 3 people smile every day, beginning with you. - Author Unknown

- Do the right thing, always! - Author Unknown

- Be content with where you are, who you are and what you have. - Author Unknown

- Practice patience, compassion and mindfulness each and every day. - Author Unknown

- You are the boss of your life, manage it well. - Author Unknown

- Slow down once in a while and take time to enjoy all the beauty around you. - Author Unknown

- It is the small gifts in life that mean the most, a sunrise, a smile, _____ (you fill in the blank) - Author Unknown

- Be open and sincere with everyone in your life. - Author Unknown

- Believe in all possibilities, the best is yet to come. - Author Unknown

- Keep your life simple, sometimes less is more. - Author Unknown

- Be kind and generous, help others every chance you get. - Author Unknown

- Each night before you sleep complete the following statement: "I am thankful for_____" - Author Unknown

- When you wake up in the morning, complete the following statement: "my purpose today is_____" – Author Unknown

- Practice being in the here and now. This is the most important moment of your life. - Author Unknown

- Patience is not the ability to wait, but the ability to keep a good attitude while waiting. - Author Unknown

- Anger doesn't solve anything. It builds nothing, but it can destroy EVERYTHING. – Thomas S Monson

- Love your parents. We are so busy growing up we often forget they are also growing old. - Author Unknown

- When problems come into your life like a non-stop rain, remember that your positive attitude will always be your umbrella. – Darshan Jain

- Holding on to anger is like grasping a hot coal with the intent of throwing it at someone else: you are the one who gets burned. - Buddha

- Thousands of candles can be lit from a single candle and the life of the candle will not be shortened. Happiness never decreases by being shared. - Buddha

- Medication makes one asleep free of worries. Meditation wakes one up to be free of worries. - Author Unknown

- Choose to discipline your breath and your body, and then you will discipline your mind. – John Ferguson

- Your worst enemy cannot harm you as much as your own unguarded thoughts. But once mastered, no one can help you as much. - Buddha

- If you light a lamp for someone else, it will also brighten your path. - Buddha

- Life is full of give and take. GIVE thanks and TAKE nothing for granted. - Author Unknown

- Don't treat people as bad as they are; treat them as good as you are. - Author Unknown

- Don't waste your words on people who deserve your silence. Sometimes the most powerful thing you can say is nothing at all. – Mandy Hale

- Patience is when you are supposed to get mad, but you choose to understand. - Author Unknown

- Watch - Lao Tzu
  o Watch your thoughts- they become words
  o Watch your words- they become actions
  o Watch your actions- they become habits
  o Watch your habits- they become character
  o Watch your character- it becomes your destiny

- What is success? Success is being able to go to bed each night with your mind at peace. – Paulo Coelho

- Never force anything. Just let it be. If it's meant to be, it will be. - Author Unknown

- Fake people have an image to maintain, real people just don't care. - Abhishek

- They laugh at me because I am different, I laugh at them because they are all the same. – Kurt Cobain

- Make each moment an occasion to live deeper, happier and in peace. – Thich Nhat Hanh

- Man sacrifices his health in order to make money. Then he sacrifices his money to recoup his health. And then he is so anxious about his future that he does not enjoy the present. The result being that he does not live in the present or the future. He lives as if he is never going to die and then dies having never really lived. - Dalai Lama

- You are not born a winner. You are not born a loser. You are born a chooser. - Author Unknown

- Happiness is not the absence of problems; it is the ability to deal with them. – Steve Maraboli

- When the actions of others no longer matter, then you have succeeded within your own mind. – Jo De Raman

- Happiness is only available in the present. – Thich Nhat Hanh

- There is not greater wealth in this world than peace of mind. - Author Unknown

- I am in competition with no one. I have no desire to play the game of being better than anyone. I am simply trying to be better than the person I was yesterday. - Author Unknown

- Control your anger, because it is just one letter away from Danger. - Author Unknown

- Family is not about blood. It is about who is willing to hold your hand when you need it the most. - Author Unknown

- A true test of character is not how you are on your best day, but on how you act on your worst. - Author Unknown

- The bad news: nothing lasts forever. The good news: nothing lasts forever. – J Cole

- We are shaped by our thoughts: we become what we think. When the mind is pure, joy follows like a shadow that never leaves. - Buddha

- Work for a cause, not applause. Live life to express, not to impress. Don't strive to make your presence noticed, just make your absence felt. - Author Unknown

- While you were waking up today, someone else was taking their last breath. Be thankful for this day, don't waste it. - Author Unknown

- Apologizing doesn't mean you're right or wrong, it just means you value your relationship more that your ego. - Author Unknown

- Ships don't sink because of the water around them. Ships sink because of the water that gets in them. Don't let what's happening around you get inside you and weigh you down. - Author Unknown

- Respect yourself enough to say, "I deserve peace" and walk away from people or things that prevent you from attaining it. – Jerico Silvers

- One of the happiest moments of your life is when you find the courage to accept what you can't change. - Author Unknown

- All that we are is the result of what we have thought. The mind is everything. What we think we become. - Buddha

- Calm your mind. Life becomes much easier when you keep your mind at peace. - Author Unknown

- I changed my thinking, and it changed my life. - Author Unknown

- Happiness does not depend on what you have or who you are. It solely relies on what you think. - Buddha

- 1 tree can make 1000 matches, but 1 match can burn 1000 trees. Moral: 1 negative thought can burn all positive thoughts- Priya Gupta

- What is STRESS? It is the gap between our expectations and reality. More the gap more the stress. So, expect nothing and accept everything. - Author Unknown

- A million things can bring you down, find ONE reason to keep you up. - Amber Afshan

- Happy people focus on what they have. Unhappy people focus on what is missing. – Karen Salmansohn

- Ikigai - (Japanese, secret to happy life) - A reason for being/living, the thing that gets you up in the morning. It's the passion that brings meaning to life.

- Never regret a day in your life: Good days give you happiness, bad days give experience, worst days give you lessons, and best days give memories. - Author Unknown

- Time is like a river. You cannot touch the same water twice, because the flow that passed will never pass again. Enjoy every moment of your life. - Author Unknown

- When you can't control what is happening, challenge yourself to control the way you respond to what is happening. That is where your power is. - Author Unknown

- Stay positive when negativity surrounds you. Smile when others refuse to. It is an easy way to make a difference in the world around. - Author Unknown

- The greatest wealth is to live content with little. - Plato

- Maturity is when you can destroy someone who did you wrong.... But you choose to breathe, walk away and let life take care. – Hugh Jackman

- The greatest stress you go through when dealing with a difficult person is not fueled by the words or actions of this person – it is fueled by your mind that gives their words and actions importance. - Author Unknown

- It is OK to be upset. It is never OK to be cruel. Rage, resentment and jealousy do not change the hearts of others, they only change yours. - Author Unknown

- Free yourself of the burden of being an eternal victim. - Author Unknown

- Gossip and drama end at a wise person's ear. Be wise. Seek to understand before you attempt to judge. Use your judgement not as a weapon for putting others down, but as a tool for making positive choices that help you build your own character. - Author Unknown

- Always set the example. Treat everyone with kindness and respect, even those who are rude to you- not because they are nice but because you are nice. Do your best to be thankful for rude and difficult people too- they serve as great reminders of how not to be. - Author Unknown

- The way we treat people we strongly disagree with is a report card on what we have learned about love, compassion and kindness. Life is too short to argue and fight. Count your blessings, value the people who matter, and move on from the drama with your head held high. - Author Unknown

- Everyone is trying to find the right person, but nobody is trying to be the right person. - Author Unknown

- Don't expect to see positive changes in your life if you constantly surround yourself with difficult people. The great danger of being around difficult people too often is that you start to become like them without even knowing it. Just because you are kind to someone, does not mean you have to spend extra time with them. - Author Unknown

- If you really want to be happy and peaceful, then stop being afraid of being yourself, and stop thinking about what others think of you every second. There is nothing selfish about giving yourself space for self-care. Experience life on your terms and you will be life-giving to others. - Author Unknown

- Take into account that great love and great achievement involve great risk. – Dalai Lama

- Never explain yourself, your real friends do not need it and your enemies will not believe it. – Belgicia Howell

- Never wish them pain. That is not who you are. If they caused you pain, they must have pain inside – Najwa Zebian

- When you are truly comfortable with whom you are, not everybody will like you. But you won't care about it one bit. - Author Unknown

- The greatest practice is PATIENCE. – John Ferguson

- If you expect people to be fair with you because you are fair with them, that is like expecting a lion not to eat you because you don't eat lions. - Author Unknown

- No matter how good or bad you think life is, wake up each day and be THANKFUL FOR LIFE, someone somewhere else is fighting to survive. - Author Unknown

- Peace is the result of retraining your mind to process life as you think it should be. – Wayne Dyer

- Keep going. The universe is guiding you. - Author Unknown

- The best revenge is to have enough self-worth not to seek it. - Author Unknown

- A smart person knows what to say. A wise person knows whether or not to say it. - Author Unknown

- You are responsible for your happiness. In fact, you create it. You attract it. You manifest it. You are the architect of your reality. You choose your thoughts, your perceptions, and your reactions to external forces. You possess all of the tools needed to expand your awareness, to choose happiness to choose love. You are that powerful. Create the life you deserve. – Creig Crippen

- The ego is not who you really are. The ego is your self-image: it is your social mask; it is the role you are playing. Your social mask thrives on approval. It wants control, and it is sustained by power, because it lives in fear. – Deepak Chopra

- The happiness of your life depends on the quality of your thoughts. – Marcus Aurelius, Roman emperor

- You don't ever have to feel guilty about removing toxic people from your life. It does not matter whether someone is a relative, romantic interest, employer, childhood friend, or a new acquaintance- you don't have to make room for people who cause you pain or make you feel small. It is one thing if a person owns up to their behavior and makes an effort to change. But if a person disregards your feelings, ignores your boundaries and continues to treat you in a harmful way, they need to go. – Danielle Koepke

- One of the biggest signs of maturity is being able to disagree with each other while still remaining respectful. – Dave Willis

- P.A.I.N.S Positive Attitude In Negative Situations. – Anjali Patole

- One day or DAY ONE? You decide. - Author Unknown

- Life is like an elevator: on your way up, you stop and let some people off. – Ziad K Abdelnour

- When you look deeply into your anger, you will see that the person you call your enemy is also suffering. As soon as you see that, the capacity for accepting and having compassion for them is there. – Thich Nhat Hanh

- SERENITY is not freedom from the storm, but the peace amid the storm. – Adrian Rogers

- Just because I do not react does not mean I did not notice. - Author Unknown

- When you come to a point where you have no need to impress anybody, your freedom will begin. - Author Unknown

- Never forget who ignored you when you needed them and who helped you before you even had to ask. - Author Unknown

- Do not take revenge. Let Karma do all the work. – Lisa Morfitt

- One breath at a time, I am not blaming my past, I am not being a victim to my past because I know now that you write your own story. You can do what you want to your story, and I will not blame myself. - Author Unknown

- There is nothing that can grow from a space of hate. - Author Unknown

- Don't let something that takes 10 seconds to say ruin the next 10 days, 10 months, or potentially 10 years of your life. - Author Unknown

- And if I asked you to name all the things you love how long would it take for you to list yourself. - Author Unknown

- Love yourself first because that is who you will spend the rest of your life with. - Author Unknown

- Low self-esteem is like driving through life with your handbrake on. - Author Unknown

- A negative mind will never give you a positive life– Ziad K. Abdelnour

- Your masterpiece comes when you master peace. - Author Unknown

- Flow with whatever may happen and let your mind be free. Stay centered by accepting whatever comes to you. -Zhuangzi

- You are the first victim of your own anger. -Nafis Ahmed

- A dream written down with a date becomes a goal. A goal broken down into steps becomes a plan. A plan backed by action becomes a reality. -Greg S Reid

- The content of your character is your choice. Day by day, what you choose what you think and what you do is who you become. -Heraclitus

- Remember the days you prayed for the things you have now. A wise man ought to realize that health is his most valuable possession. - Author Unknown

- If people love me, they are welcome; if they hate me, they are also welcome. -Swami Vivekananda

- Faith is not about everything turning out ok. Faith is about being ok no matter how it turns out. - Author Unknown

- Self-control is strength. Right thought is mastery. Calmness is power. – James Allen

- DEAR SELF- don't get worked up over things you can't change, people you can't change. It's not worth buildup of the headache. Control only what you can. Let go. - Author Unknown

- Forgiveness is unlocking the door to set someone free and realizing you were the prisoner. -Max Lucado

- However, many holy words you read, however many you speak, what good will they do you if you do not act upon them. - Buddha

- You will continue to suffer if you have an emotional reaction to everything that is said to you. True power is sitting back & observing everything with logic. True power is restraint. If words control you that means everyone else can control you. Breathe and allow things to pass. – Jawad Abid

- Don't worry about needing a lot of stuff.... In the end all you really need is to be happy. - Author Unknown

- The mind is everything. What you think you become. - Buddha

- We need suffering in order to see the path to healing. The origin of suffering, the cessation of suffering, and the path leading to cessation of suffering are all found in the heart of suffering. If we are afraid to touch our suffering, we will not be able to realize the path to peace, joy, and liberation. Don't run away. Touch your suffering and embrace it. Make peace with it. - Author Unknown

- The best answer to anger is silence- Marcus Aurelius

- The moment you accept what troubles you have been given; the door opens. - Rumi

- People are not addicted to alcohol or drugs; they are addicted to escaping reality. - Author Unknown

- There are many ways to calm a negative energy without suppressing or fighting it. You recognize it, you smile to it and invite something nicer to come up and replace it. You read some inspiring words, you listen to music, you go somewhere in nature, or you do some walking meditation. -Thich Nhat Hanh

- Once a wise man was asked... "What is the meaning of life"? He replied life itself has no meaning; life is an opportunity to create meaning. - Author Unknown

- We all die one day, the goal is not to live forever, the goal is to create something that will. -Chuck Palahniuk

- Explain your anger, don't express it and you will immediately open the door to solutions instead of arguments. - Author Unknown

- Knowledge comes from learning; Wisdom comes from living. -A. D. Williams

- A strong emotion is like a storm. You should not wait for emotions to appear before you begin practicing calm. Otherwise you will be carried away by the storm. - Author Unknown

- Religion is for people concerned with going to hell. Spirituality is for those who have already been there. – Vine Deloria

- Not all storms come to disrupt your life; some come to clear your path. - Author Unknown

- How does it feel to be so weak minded that a word or opinion can control you? - Author Unknown

- The real test is being kind to unkind people. - Author Unknown

- When other people treat you poorly, keep being you. Don't ever let someone else's bitterness change the person you are. - Author Unknown

- Worry about your character, not your reputation. Because your character is who you are, while your reputation is merely what others think you are. -John Wooden

- If you can't fly then run, if you can't run then walk, if you can't walk then crawl, but whatever you do you have to keep moving forward. – Martin Luther King Jr

- And then it happens.... One day you wake up and you're in this place. You're in this place where everything feels right. Your heart is calm, your soul is lit, your thoughts are positive, and your vision is clear. You're at peace, at peace with where you've been, at peace with what you've been through and at peace with where you're heading. - Author Unknown

153

- Anger is the feeling that makes your mouth work faster than your mind. – Evan Esar

- Positive people also have negative thoughts. They just don't allow those thoughts to control them. - Author Unknown

- Your problems may be great, but my strength within is far greater. - Author Unknown

- How others see you is not important. How you see yourself means everything. - Author Unknown

- When you are right, you have no need to be angry. When you are wrong, you have no right to be angry. – Mahatma Gandhi

- Let there be action without reaction. Action is pleasant, misery is reaction. - Author Unknown

- The true purpose of ZEN is to see things as they are, to observe things as they are, and to let everything go as it goes. Zen practice is to open up our small mind. – Shunryu Suzuki

- One of the hardest lessons in life is letting go. Whether it is guilt, anger, love, loss or betrayal. Change is never easy; we fight to hold on and we fight to let go. – Mareez Reyes

- The only people with whom you should try to get even with are those who helped you. – John E Southard

- Turn your wounds into wisdom- Simon Reed

- Everything - including love, hate, and suffering needs food to continue. If suffering continues, it's because we keep feeding our suffering. Thich Nhat Hanh

- Ultimately the source of happiness and joy is within us. - Author Unknown

- The hardest battle is between what you know in your head and what you feel in your heart. - Author Unknown

- The weak never can forgive. Forgiveness is the attribute of the strong. Tension is who you think you should be. Relaxation is who you are. - Author Unknown

- Meditation can turn fools into sages, but unfortunately fools never meditate. -Swami Vivekananda

- Meditation is the journey from SOUND to Silence... From limited identity to UNLIMITED -Sri Ravi Shankar

- A man who committed a mistake and doesn't correct it is committing another mistake. -Confucius

- Two things define you: Your patience when you have nothing and your attitude when you have everything. - Author Unknown

- One of the marvels of the world is the sight of a soul sitting in prison with the key in their hand. -Rumi

- Why is this happening to me??? What is this teaching me? - Author Unknown

- What you need, what we all need, is silence. Stop the noise in your mind in order for the wondrous sounds of life to be heard. – Thich Nhat Hanh

- The cave you fear to enter holds the treasure that you seek. – Joseph Campbell

- A saint was asked- "what is anger"? He gave a beautiful answer. "It is a punishment we give to our self, for the mistakes of another. - Author Unknown

- Pain travels through family lines until someone is ready to heal it in themselves. By going through the agony of healing you no longer pass the poison behavior onto the next generation. It is incredibly important and sacred work. - Author Unknown

- Compassion is not complete if it does not include oneself. -Buddha

- You will never speak to anyone more that you speak to yourself in your head, be kind to yourself. -Amardeep Kumar

- The relationship you have with yourself sets the tone for every other relationship you have. - Author Unknown

- How will you know when you are making progress? When what once made you mad now makes you laugh. - Author Unknown

- Your ego is not your amigo - Author Unknown

- Only he, who knows what is enough, will always have enough. – Lao Tzu

- Inner peace begins the moment you choose not to allow another person or event to control your emotions. – Pema Chodron

- Replacing "I'm sorry" with "thank you". So instead of saying "Sorry I was late", say "thank you for waiting for me" replacing negative with positive and gratitude and break the "I'm sorry" cycle. - Author Unknown

- I may not be where I want to be, but I'm thankful for not being where I used to be. Habeeb Akande

- If you don't change direction, you may end up where you are heading. -Lao Tzu

- Your problem is not the problem; your reaction is the problem. - Author Unknown

- Before you heal someone, ask him if he's willing to give up the things that made him sick. -Hippocrates

- Truth is like a surgery. It hurts, but cures. A Lie is like a pain killer. It gives relief, but has side effects forever. - Buddha

- Protect yourself from your own thoughts. - Rumi

- Loosing someone who doesn't respect or appreciate you is your gain and their loss. - Author Unknown

- The best revenge is no revenge. Just forget they exist. – Buddha

- Change is never painful. Only the resistance to change is painful. – Buddha

- Your value doesn't decrease based on someone's inability to see your worth. – Author Unknown

- Avoiding your triggers isn't healing. Healing happens when you're triggered and you're able to move through the pain, pattern, and the story and walk your way to a different ending. – Vienna Pharaon

- He who blames others has a long way on his journey. He who blames himself is halfway there. He who blames no one has arrived. – Chinese proverb

- The true hero is one who conquers his own anger and hatred. – Dalai Lama

- We repeat what we don't repair. - Sujata Agarwal

- Often, it's the deepest pain which empowers you to grow into your highest self. – Karen Salmansohn

- Until you heal the wounds of your past, you are going to bleed. You can bandage the bleeding with food, alcohol, drugs, work, cigarettes, and sex. But eventually, it will all ooze through and stain your life. You must find the strength to open the wound, stick your hands inside, pull out the core of the pain that is holding you in your past, the memories and make peace with them. – Author Unknown

- Never let a bad situation bring out the worst in you. Choose to stay positive. – Author Unknown

- People were created to be loved. Things were created to be used. The reason the world is in chaos is because things are being loved and people are being used. – Dalai Lama

- Do you have the patience to wait until your mind settles and the water clears? Can you remain unmoving until the right action arises by itself? – Lao Tzu (Tao Te Ching)

- PEACE- It does not mean to be in a place with no noise, trouble or challenges. It means to be in the midst of those things and still be calm in your heart. – Author Unknown

- Forgive yourself for not knowing better at the time. Forgive yourself for giving away your power. Forgive yourself for the past behaviors. Forgive yourself for the survival patterns and traits you picked up while enduring trauma. Forgive yourself for being who you needed to be. – Audrey Kitching

- Grace means that all of your mistakes now serve a purpose instead of serving shame. – Brene Brown

- Negative people need drama like oxygen. Stay positive, it will take their breath away. – Author Unknown

- A happy person is happy, not because everything is right in their life. They are happy because their attitude towards everything in their life is right. – Buddha

- I learned that every mortal will taste death. But only some will taste life. – Author Unknown

159

- If you don't change the direction you are going. Then you're likely to end up where you're heading. – John Maxwell

- Nobody makes you angry. You decide to use anger as a response. – Book of Serenity

- Meditation is about learning to work with the mind as it is, not about trying to force it into some sort of Buddhist straitjacket. – Yongey Mingyur Rinpoche

- If you can't handle stress, you can't handle success. – Author Unknown

- Much suffering, much unhappiness arises when you take each thought that comes into your head for the truth. – Eckhart Tolle

- There is nothing noble in being superior to your fellow man. True nobility lies in being superior to your former self. – Ernest Hemingway

- Care about what other people think and you will always be their prisoner. – Lao Tzu

- Don't be afraid of losing people. Be afraid of losing yourself by trying to please everyone around you. – Author Unknown

- Every day is another chance to change your life. – Author Unknown

- Weak people seek revenge. Strong people forgive. Intelligent people ignore. – Buddha

- When you find peace within yourself, you become the kind of person who can live at peace with others. – Anne Frank

- The most important spiritual growth doesn't happen when you are in meditation or on the yoga mat. It happens in the mist of conflict when you're frustrated, angry or scared and you're doing the same old thing, and then you suddenly realize that you have a choice to do it differently. – Author Unknown

- EGO says, "once everything falls into place, I'll feel peace". SPIRIT says, "find peace and then everything will fall into place". – Author Unknown

- You have power over your mind- not outside events. Realize this and you will find strength. – Marcus Aurelius

- Never hold your farts in. They travel up your spine, into your brain and that's where shitty ideas come from. – Author Unknown

- You can only win when your mind is stronger than your emotions. – Author Unknown

- You have to get to a point where your mood doesn't shift based on the insignificant actions of someone else. Don't allow others to control the direction of your life. Don't allow your emotions to overpower your intelligence. – Author Unknown

- The best revenge is to improve yourself. – Buddha

- When you discover something that heals you and brings happiness, care enough about yourself to make room for it in your daily life. – Author Unknown

- It's beautiful to be alone. To be alone does not mean to be lonely. It means the mind is not influenced and contaminated by society. – Jiddu Krishnamurti

- Truth is not what you want it to be, it is what it is and you must bend to its power or live a lie. – Miyamoto Musashi

- You either get bitter or better. It's that simple. You either take what has been dealt to you or allow it to make you a better person or you allow it to tear you down. The choice does not belong to fate, it belongs to you. – Buddha

- Our brains are wired for connection, but trauma rewires them for protection. That's why healthy relationships are difficult for the wounded people. – Ryan North

- So far, you've survived 100% of your worst days. You're doing great. – Author Unknown

- The version of me you create in your mind is not my responsibility. Anonymous

- A person that isn't at peace with them will be at war with the rest of the world. – Author Unknown

- How much more grievous are the consequences of anger than the causes of it. – Marcus Aurelius

162

- I sat with my anger long enough; until it told me its real name was _____ (you fill in the blank). – Author Unknown

- If you focus on the hurt, you will continue to suffer. If you focus on the lesson, you will continue to grow. – Buddha

- Fall seven times, stand up eight. – Japanese proverb

- You never know how strong you are until being strong is your only choice. -Bob Marley

- Some of us think holding on makes us strong, but sometimes it is letting go. – Hermann Hesse

- Life is truly known only to those who suffer, lose, endure adversity and stumble from defeat to defeat. – Anais Nin

- There are two ways of exerting one's strength, one is pushing down the other is pulling up. – Booker T Washington

- Let me tell you the secret that has led me to my goal: my strength lies solely in my Tenacity. – Louis Pasteur

- With the right attitude, self-imposed limitations vanish. – Alexander the Great

- Courage isn't having the strength to go on; it is going on when you don't have the strength. – Napoleon Bonaparte

163

- The true hero is one who conquers their own anger and hatred. – Dalai Lama

- Continuous effort- Not strength or intelligence is the key to unlocking our potential. – Winston Churchill

- Before you argue with someone, think to yourself is this person even mentally mature enough to grasp the concept of different perspectives. Because if not, there is no point. – Author Unknown

- You can't change what is going on around you, until you start changing what is going on within you. – Author Unknown

- Holding on to anger is like drinking poison an expecting the other person to die. - Buddha

- Your teacher can open the door, but you must enter by yourself. – Chinese proverb

- Possession of material riches, without inner peace, is like dying of thirst while bathing in a lake. – Paramahansa Yogananda

- One day it just clicks... you realize what's important and what is not. You learn to care less what other people think about you and more about what you think of yourself. You realize how far you've come, and you remember when you thought things were such a mess that you would never recover. And you smile. You smile because you are truly proud of yourself and the person you've fought to become. - Author Unknown

- I cannot teach anybody anything; I can only make them think. – Socrates

- The two most important days of your life are the day you are born... and the day you find out why.   -Mark Twain
- There is nothing outside of yourself that can ever enable you to get better, stronger, richer, quicker, or smarter. Everything is within. – Miyamoto Musashi

- But where life is more terrible that death, it is then the truest valor to dare to live. – Inazo Nitobe (Author of Bushido)

- Do not pray for an easy life. Pray for the strength to endure a difficult one. – Bruce Lee

- All men die, but not all men really live. – William Wallace

- Yesterday was my day to die. Today is my day to live- John Ferguson

16 FOR THE FAMILY

My spouse, friend or loved one left as one person, and seems to have come back as a totally different stranger! How can I connect with this person who seems to have zero patience and goes from okay one moment to totally angry in the next?

When your loved one suffers from PTS this book can help the whole family. This section is built so that the support network has tools to cope with a person suffering from PTS and to help them heal.

Before heading off to combat, deployments, schools, trainings or dangerous situations, your loved one may have acted one way. After their return they now act differently. They may suffer with symptoms of PTS; anger, depression, fog, isolation, detachment, hypervigilance, anxiety or a myriad of other challenging symptoms.

Indeed, they do act differently. However, I will suggest that not only are they different, but *you* are also different. Each person is built by their experiences. Your experiences, while they were away, have changed you. You became used to running the household, getting together with friends and your support network, holding down a job, or teaching the children in your way. Now the two of you are back together and working things out.

First you have your honeymoon stage where you are happy to be back together and are extra careful to not rock the boat. The honeymoon stage will not last forever, so enjoy it while you can.

Both of you have changed. Change can be very difficult for some people. When things change it can cause frustration, irritability and anger. Then PTS symptoms rear their ugly head and cause even more aggravation and change.

Consider this, when someone has a traumatic experience, there are resulting feelings and behaviors you may not like. Your spouse or loved one did not ask for these traumatic experiences and certainly would like to avoid the mental, emotional or physical issues that follow. Neither of you want these negative behaviors. Just remember, it is the traumatic experience that created the PTS and it is that event that is at fault, not your loved one.

Try to have patience and tolerance while they are trying to work through their traumatic experiences. Your partner may not be able to discuss their experiences. The experiences may have affected them so greatly that it is difficult to discuss. In addition, your veteran may feel that you just *do not* and *cannot* understand what happened. They have created such a bond and brotherhood or sisterhood that it may unintentionally exclude you.

There are a couple of ways to handle your desire to hear their experiences. First, try patience. Your spouse will start to tell you things about the experiences in time. Don't rush in with a lot of questions. This brings frustration and anger into the mix. Instead, focus on the now.

Another way to hear about what happened while they were away is to focus on the feelings instead of the event. What little your veteran may be able to tell you will help guide you on this path. Instead of phrasing the question as, "How do you feel about that?" empathize with him or her about the circumstances. Show gratitude for your loved one sharing the stories. Appreciate that sharing the experiences that cause PTS is difficult to do. Such as:

"Thank you for telling me a little about how you feel."
"Hearing your story helps me to understand a little better."

Sympathy is when you share the other person's feelings. You feel happy about something they are happy about. Sharing happiness is good. Sharing sadness over a misfortune is good. Empathy is when you acknowledge your veteran's feelings, but do not share their feelings. You experience different feelings such as concern or confusion while the veteran is feeling depressed or angry.

Express how you are feeling and share your happiness. Share small and big things that show appreciation for the surroundings, such as a beautiful sunset or funny shaped clouds.

Dealing with Angry Outbursts: You may want to have a safe word. A safe word is for *you* when you feel that the situation is out of control or for *the veteran* when he or she feels out of control. The safe word should be something you do not say often, but can be used in regular conversation without sounding ridiculous. One example could be an infrequently used word. If you never eat donuts or guacamole, use donuts or guacamole as your safe word. The word is up to you. Be aware that sometimes the emotion and anger may be so great, that your veteran may not be able to remember the safe word none-the-less be able to use the safe word. Lastly, the safe word is something used when it is essential for your mental, physical or emotional safety.

Try to understand that your veteran does not have self-control at that moment. The anger will appear to go from zero to one hundred percent. Zero percent and things appear fine. You are rolling along and content. Then seemingly out of the blue there is a huge angry outburst and the anger lashes out. The anger is lashing out to anyone and everyone. The anger is not all negative, but it can be confusing, frustrating and make you want to return fire with fire. I don't recommend returning with angry responses.

The good part about the anger is that your veteran feels safe to display the anger with you and knows he or she has your support. Wait until later to discuss, as calmly as possible, your concerns and the modifications you would like to see. Remove the **'not'** and ask for changes with patience and positivity.

Phrasing your requests in a positive way can help. Try to untie frustration with this idea. Use something other than 'not'. Instead of saying, "Do **not** _____.", try "Can you **do** _____." 'Do not bring your shoes in the house' changes to 'Can you set your shoes at the front door'. Yes, there may be repetition. Yes, there may be frustration. Not all days are clear and sometimes the memory does not work well. It is what it is. What you do with the situation will make all of the difference.

You can meet together when things are calmer and create goals or make a plan. If this _____ happens, then this _____ will be the plan. Having a plan will allow you not to only react, but to prepare and respond.

Expectations: One of the more difficult aspects of communication is when two different people have varying expectations. When you are feeling a certain way, whether it is angry or happy, you see others through that emotional lens. It is easier to see other people happy if you are happy or feel that someone is slighting you if you are angry. The same occurs between you and your loved one. That emotional lens is exaggerated when your loved one has PTS.

One helpful method is to create a transition for yourself so that you do not have a specific expectation. For example, you are heading home from work and your loved one is at home. When you are transitioning between being by yourself and with your loved one try the following: turn off your radio a mile or so away from your home and try to eliminate whatever expectations you may have about what will greet you when you get home. Just because you are happy or angry at something that happened at work doesn't mean that your loved one will be happy or angry also. Perhaps you are both happy. The point is that there is no way to know what will greet you when you get home. Give yourself that time to breathe and relax.

Communication: No matter how long you have known each other, clear and complete communication can be tough to achieve. Use **CCMU**. Clear Complete Mutual Understanding. Communication (CCMU) may sound simple, but it is fraught with misunderstandings. When communication is not *Clear* it sounds like this: "Can you take that over there?" The 'that' and 'there' are not clear. Instead, "Could you take the dish and place it in the center of the table?" is clearer.

Secondly, *Complete* shows that all the necessary parts of the question or statement is there. For example, "Could you take the dish and place it in the center of the table?" is not complete if there are several dishes ready to go on the table. A question stated like the following is complete: "Could you take the blue serving dish and place it in the center of the table?"

Mutual understanding may seem like an easy concept. However, have you ever had two people tell you about something they both saw occur? People have different perspectives and take in information in slightly different ways. Here is an example. One person sees a finished project in their mind before the project starts. The other person also sees the project. Unless you have a mutual understanding there can be confusion, frustration, and you got it, ANGER!

Lastly, you can bring about positive change by complimenting and appreciating when things are going well. Try not to take your loved one for granted. Everyone likes to hear they are doing well and likes to be appreciated. Be willing to help, offer support and understanding. When your veteran knows that you support them, it means a lot.

Dealing with Isolation or Detachment: Was your spouse, friend or loved one an extrovert? Did they enjoy spending time with others? Was your veteran an introvert and spent time with a small closely knit group of friends and family. Either way, it is likely that there will be changes after PTS occurs.

After a traumatic occurrence, your loved one may want to isolate and detach from other relationships; maybe even from you and the family. While the isolation and detachment may be mild or severe, these symptoms of PTS are one way for your loved one to start dealing with their traumatic event. It is likely that your veteran will feel alone and feels like the first person that is going through the process. Feeling alone or isolated is not the same thing as loneliness.

This is where a good support network for **you** is important. If you have a good support network, you will have someone with whom you can release some good-natured complaining. Being able to vent your feelings will help you to cope.

There are ways to help with the feelings of isolation or detachment. Make it easy for your loved one to join into activities. Allow the veteran to know that it is okay if he or she feels uncomfortable in joining. Offer acceptance. Try not to add a feeling of guilt for not joining in activities that you are doing.

Not all combat situations are negative. The camaraderie and support network they created can benefit your loved one. That network could help the transition from combat life to civilian life. Creating a collage of combat pictures that show the good times may help that transition.

Other ways to help with detachment and isolation could be: reaching out to or helping other former veterans or friends, offering a safe place, recommending meditation, joining a veteran group, suggesting exercise, seeking counseling, volunteering, etc. The important part is that you are being proactive. You know your loved one, even though there have been changes for both of you. Therefore, you have the knowledge of what to try and what may work best. Most important is encourage connections; connections with you, friends, family, children, other military members, the church or whatever works.

Dealing with the Fog: Veterans may show signs of confusion or Fog; especially with Traumatic Brain Injury (TBI) and PTS. How do you deal with your loved one forgetting how to do basic things, like tie shoes? First and foremost remember, it is not their fault. A traumatic experience occurred and caused these symptoms. The best way to deal with confusion and fog is to accept that at that moment, that hour, that day or that week your loved one is not able to think clearly. You could offer the following:

1. There are challenges with memory or basic tasks at the moment.
2. The challenges are not all of the time.
3. You accept the challenges and will work together.

This is a great time to think out of the box. Can't tie your shoes? Get slip-on shoes. Can't seem to remember events? Put the event on a calendar and set reminders or alarms. Need to remember to take something to snack on or drink when leaving the house? Put a post-it or sticky note on the door. Every problem has a solution.

Dealing with Anxiety or Hypervigilance: Everyone has stress. Change can cause stress and stress causes anxiety. Anxiety is the **natural** reaction to stressful situations. Your stress may be a move, new job or school, dealing with family or something else. The symptoms of your stress may or may not be as severe as the list of hypervigilance, fog, anger, detachment, isolation or other symptoms. Remembering that you *also* have stresses and anxiety in your life can help you to problem solve and have empathy for your loved one.

Having someone around you that is supernaturally aware and tuned in to the surrounding situation may be challenging for you. There is a difference between being situationally aware and being hypervigilant. Hypervigilance starts with situation awareness. Being aware of whatever situation your veteran is in, means that they notice everything around them. And I do mean everything.

Hypervigilance means that your veteran is experiencing the same thing as situational awareness, but the difference is in their response. Trash on the side of the road may be a roadside bomb so they may veer away toward the other

174

side of the road. Someone standing behind or walking towards them may appear menacing. Sudden noises may startle them and cause them to turn and prepare to fight.

Some of these behaviors have easy fixes. Don't stand behind your loved or make noise when you approach. Offering a quiet place where they can decompress can help. Other things will take more patience and tolerance.

Remember, hypervigilance is not bad. It is trained, ingrained and allowed your veteran to survive. Hypervigilance is one way that your loved one managed to come back to you. This path managing PTS can be difficult. Forgive each other your mistakes. Try again. Together you can accomplish anything.

Try to be patient.

Try to be understanding.

Note the key word is to **try**.

ABOUT THE AUTHOR

John Ferguson is still on his path to healing. It is a long process and will take time, but it nice to still have time. He lives in Virginia with his wife of 28 years. He will dedicate the remaining days to helping other vets find their path. He hopes you will reach out and open up about your struggles.

<u>Support network:</u> Please go to my Facebook page Facebook.com/Living Beyond PTS and join the group. I want to hear your comments, what works and what doesn't. This is our way to connect worldwide and speak our minds. I would like input for additional quotes and what quotes worked for you.

Thank you.

This book guides anyone seeking to relieve stress and find peace, in a simple and straightforward manner. The artwork gives readers a visual understanding of the anguish too many people feel. John makes it easy to practice on your own by creating an acronym-CENTER-to guide your process.

John has written a remarkable book. From his personal struggles, adjusting back to civilian life, following too many combat tours, John searched for, and found a highly successful method to bring back calm and peace of mind.

I also very much enjoyed the life guiding quotes he provided. The book mentions John's singing bowls, truly they need to be experienced to appreciate their powerful calming power.

- Frank, 11th Marines Vietnam 1970-1971

Made in the USA
Middletown, DE
09 May 2023